medin

CLIMBING

HIGHER

Pathway Publishers

Aylmer, Ontario - LaGrange, Indiana

PATHWAY READING SERIES

FIRST STEPS, 140 pages   Grade 1
DAYS GO BY, 158 pages   Grade 1
MORE DAYS GO BY, 170 pages   Grade 1
BUSY TIMES, 249 pages   Grade 2
MORE BUSY TIMES, 288 pages   Grade 2
CLIMBING HIGHER, 248 pages   Grade 2
NEW FRIENDS, 284 pages   Grade 3
MORE NEW FRIENDS, 288 pages   Grade 3
BUILDING OUR LIVES, 496 pages   Grade 4
LIVING TOGETHER, 527 pages   Grade 5
STEP BY STEP, 416 pages   Grade 6
SEEKING TRUE VALUES, 464 pages   Grade 7
OUR HERITAGE, 478 pages   Grade 8

An accompanying workbook for this
textbook is available from:

Pathway Publishers
2580N 250W
LaGrange, IN 46761

Printed in U.S.A.

CONTENTS

Unit Four — CLIMBING HIGHER

Unit One:

Day By Day

Too Little

Part 1: Making Plans

"Oh, Mother, the hay smells so good. I wish I could go out and play in it," said Wilma. She had just come back from taking a drink to the men.

"Let's finish these strawberries, then you can play until it is time to chore," Mother promised.

Wilma worked fast. She finished cleaning the berries and then she washed

6

jars for Mother. Soon Dad and the boys came in with another load of hay. Wilma took them another drink of fresh water. Since the work in the house was done, Mother said Wilma could stay out to play.

When Amos heard that Wilma had time to play, he decided not to go along to the field. Wilma was glad, because playing would be more fun if Amos stayed there to play with her. He didn't help in the field. He just went along for the ride.

Wilma was seven years old, and Amos was five. He was the youngest in the family. Samuel, the next boy, was eight. They often played with each other, but today Samuel could not play. He had to drive the horses to load the hay.

Wilma and Amos played in the hay. They had a good time. They pretended they were wild animals and dug into the hay to make nests. It was while Wilma was lying in her nest that she had an idea. "It would be fun to sleep out here," she said. "I am going to ask Samuel to sleep out here with me."

"Oh, that would be fun," Amos said.
"I want to sleep out here, too."

"But you are too little," Wilma said.
"You would be afraid. It gets very dark
in the barn at night."

"I'm not afraid," Amos said quickly.

"Mother won't let you sleep out here," Wilma said. She sounded very old and wise. "I am sure she will say you are too little. You see, Samuel and I are much older than you are."

"Only two years," Amos said.

"But that is a lot," Wilma said. "I was five a long, long time ago. I can hardly remember it."

Amos sighed. It seemed he was always too little to do the things he wanted to do. Dad said he was too little to drive the horses. Mother said he was too little to milk a cow by himself. Wilma said he was too little to do a lot of things.

Amos ran to the house. "Samuel and Wilma are going to sleep in the barn to-night," he told Mother. "I want to sleep out there, too."

"What are Samuel and Wilma going to do?" asked Mother. She sounded very surprised.

"They are going to sleep in the barn," Amos answered.

"Who said they are?" Mother asked.

"Wilma did and I —" Amos started to say.

"Wilma was just talking," Mother said. She got out a bowl and put some sugar into it. "How would you like to have some strawberry shortcake for supper?"

Amos was not thinking about what he wanted for supper. He was thinking about sleeping in the barn. "May I sleep in the barn if Samuel and Wilma do?" he asked.

"Run along and play," Mother said. "We will talk about this later."

When Samuel came in from the field, Wilma asked him if he wanted to sleep in the barn. Of course, he did. He was just as excited about it as Wilma was.

Amos kept saying that he was going to sleep in the barn, too. Wilma kept saying he was too little. When he did not change his mind, she told him about the things that might happen to him in the barn. He might hear funny noises. He might not be able to sleep all night. There were mice in the barn. Maybe a mouse would come and bite his toe.

All this did not make Amos change his mind. He still wanted to sleep in the barn.

At first Mother did not want to hear a word about it. "Why would you want to sleep in the barn?" she asked. "The house is the place for you to sleep." But then when she saw how excited the children were, she said she and Dad would talk it over.

"Oh, I hope we may! I hope we may!" said Amos, jumping up and down.

"Even if Samuel and I may, I do not think Dad and Mother will let you sleep in the barn," Wilma said. "You are too little."

But Wilma was mistaken. Dad and Mother decided that all three of the children could sleep in the barn. "If you are afraid, you can come into the house," Dad said to Amos. "The moon will be shining, so you will be able to find the way. My guess is you will all come in as soon as it gets dark."

"Not I," said Wilma. "I am not afraid.
If Amos is afraid to come to the house by
himself, I will come with him. But I will
go back to the barn to sleep."

"Don't talk too big," Dad said. "Maybe Amos will have to come to the house
with you."

"Oh, no! I'm not afraid. I'm sure I
won't come in," answered Wilma.

The children could hardly wait until it
was time to go to bed. The sun was still
shining when they took their blankets and
went to the barn. "I'm going to sleep in
this corner," Wilma said. She put down

her blanket and dug into the soft green hay. Soon she had a nice little nest to sleep in.

The boys could not decide where they were going to sleep. Amos wanted to sleep close to Samuel, but he did not want to say so. He was afraid the other children would laugh at him and say he had to go to the house.

At last they each had a nest and were ready to sleep. But no one was sleepy. They played in the hay, then Samuel told a story. The children had a good time. "This is fun," Samuel said. "I hope we may sleep in the barn every night."

Part 2: Who Is Afraid?

The sun went down behind the woods. Soon it began to get dark. The barn did not look right anymore. It had deep shadows and dark corners. Wilma did not feel like playing now. "I'm going to sleep," she said.

"So am I," said both boys.

Soon everything was quiet. Wilma lay
still, trying hard to sleep. It was very
dark in the barn by now, but when Wilma
turned her head she could see the open
barn doors. The moon was shining, and it
was not so dark on the outside.

Suddenly Wilma thought of something —
snakes! If there was anything she was
afraid of, it was snakes. The very
thought of them made her feel cold all
over. What if a snake came into the barn
tonight and curled up beside her? Maybe
she should go close the barn doors to keep
out the snakes.

Then Wilma thought of something else.
What if the snake was already in the barn?
Maybe it had come in with the hay that
day. Maybe it was coming toward her
right now. She could almost feel its cold,
smooth skin on her bare legs.

Wilma curled up into her blanket a little tighter, but it was of no use. She could not sleep. How could she sleep when there was a snake in the barn?

Very quietly Wilma crept out of the barn. The next minute she was running toward the house as fast as she could go. There was a light in the house, so she knew Dad and Mother had not gone to bed. She burst into the house and started to cry.

"What's wrong?" Mother asked. "What happened?"

"The snakes, Mother! I'm afraid of the snakes," sobbed Wilma.

"Snakes!" cried Mother, jumping up from her chair. "Where are they?"

"In the barn. On the hay. They came in on the wagon today." Wilma could not stop crying.

Dad, who had been reading, put down his book. "Did you see them?" he asked.

"No, I didn't see them, but I am sure they are there," Wilma said. She felt a little silly now, but she didn't care. She wasn't going to sleep out there in that old barn.

"Are the boys sleeping?" Mother asked.

"I don't know," Wilma said. "I — I didn't tell them I am coming in."

A little later Wilma was in her bed. It was not as soft as the hay had been, but it felt nice and warm. "The house is the best place to sleep," she thought as she was going to sleep. "There are no snakes in the house."

All this while there was someone else in the barn who could not sleep. It was Samuel. He was not afraid of the dark, and he was not afraid of snakes. But there was something else he was afraid of. As he lay on the fresh hay, he remembered that a barn had burned down last summer. Dad had explained that the hay had not been dry enough when it was put into that barn. It had gotten so hot that it caught fire.

Samuel did not want to think about it, but he could not help it. The hay had not been very dry that day. What if it got hot overnight and caught fire? The thought was almost too terrible to think about.

It was not long until Samuel decided he did not want to sleep in the barn after all. He sat up and looked around. He could see Amos, and he knew in which corner Wilma was. Maybe if he was very quiet, he could slip out of the barn without the others knowing it. They could sleep in the barn if they wanted to, but he would not.

Outside the barn Samuel stopped. If the barn was going to burn down, he did not want to have Wilma and Amos in it. Should he go back and make them come in with him? But no, if he did that, they would think he was afraid to go to the house by himself.

The house was dark now. Samuel opened the door slowly and softly. He hoped he could slip upstairs and go to bed without being heard. But he was just inside the door when he heard Mother's voice. "Amos."

Samuel stood still. Then he said, "It's not Amos. It's me."

Mother did not sound surprised. "Where is Amos?"

"Out in the barn," answered Samuel.

"Did you leave him all by himself?"
Mother asked.

"No, Wilma's out with him," Samuel
answered.

"Wilma is not with him. She is upstairs
in her bed," Mother said. "You aren't
going to leave Amos out in the barn all
by himself."

"Is Amos sleeping?" asked Dad.

"I don't know," Samuel said. "I didn't
ask him." He was afraid Mother would
make him go out and sleep with Amos.

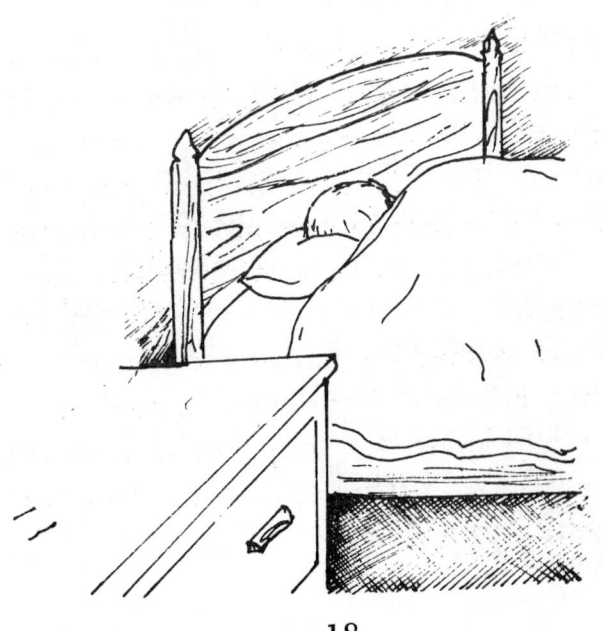

18

"Go to bed," Dad said. "Amos will come in before long."

Samuel went upstairs and curled up under the covers. It was not really cold, but the covers still felt good. "This is such a good place to sleep, I can not understand why I thought I wanted to sleep in the barn," he thought.

Part 3: One Brave Boy

All this while Amos was still awake. He was not sleepy. Everything seemed so strange. There were noises he was not used to. The smell of the fresh hay reminded him that he was not in the house. Why did he think he wanted to sleep in the barn?

Amos wished he had stayed in the house, but he did not want Samuel and Wilma to know it. They would think that he was just a little boy if they found out that he was afraid.

Then Amos thought of something. Once he had been afraid to go to the cellar by himself. Mother had told him that God sends his angels to take care of little children. After that he had not been afraid.

"If the angels can take care of me in the house, they can take care of me out here, too," he thought. He opened his eyes and looked around. He did not see an angel, but he saw the moon and the stars through the open barn doors. It did not seem quite so dark now, and Amos did not feel afraid. "Wilma and Samuel are with me," he thought. Soon he was asleep.

20

Amos slept soundly. He did not hear or
see a thing when a big man came into the
barn. He did not even see the light that
flashed on and off a few times. The man
found Samuel's blanket. He wrapped himself into it and lay down beside Amos.

It was sometime during the night that
Amos awoke. At first he did not know
where he was, but then he remembered.
He was sleeping in the barn. He rolled
over and felt someone beside him. "Oh,
good. Samuel came over to sleep beside
me," he thought. Then he went back to
sleep.

The next time Amos awoke, the sun
was shining. He sat up and looked
around. He saw that he was alone.
"Samuel and Wilma are up already," he
thought. Quickly he jumped up and ran
to the house.

The others were just ready to eat breakfast when Amos burst into the kitchen.
"Good morning, Amos," said Dad in a
big voice. "Did you sleep well?"

"Oh, yes," answered Amos. "It was fun sleeping in the barn." Then he looked at Samuel and Wilma. "Why didn't you wake me? I wanted to get up when you did."

Wilma looked at Samuel and Samuel looked at Wilma. No one said a word. At last Dad said, "They changed their minds and decided not to sleep in the barn after all. They woke up in the house this morning, and not in the barn."

22

Amos's eyes got big. Were the others playing some kind of trick on him? "I — I didn't sleep out there by myself, did I?" he asked. And then he remembered. "Samuel was there. I am sure he was, because I woke up and felt him beside me."

Dad chuckled and chuckled. "That wasn't Samuel," he said.

"Then who was it?" Amos asked.

"It was Dad," Mother said. "I wanted him to go out and bring you in so you wouldn't be by yourself. But instead of doing that, he went out and slept with you."

"But why did Samuel and Wilma come in?" asked Amos.

"Sometimes people aren't as brave as they think they are," Dad said. "Were you afraid?"

Amos looked at the floor. "A little," he said slowly. "But I didn't go in. I didn't want Samuel and Wilma to laugh at me."

"This is one time when you can laugh at Samuel and Wilma," Mother said. "Even though they often talk about being older and bigger than you are, you were the only one who was brave enough to sleep in the barn."

"What about me?" asked Dad. "I slept in the barn, too."

"Were you afraid, Dad?" asked Samuel.

"Afraid? Why should I have been afraid when I had a brave fellow like Amos with me?" He sat down at the table and winked at Amos.

Amos grinned and grinned. He was very pleased with himself. As for Wilma, she did not say a word. It was a long time until she told Amos he was too little to do the things she and Samuel did.

The Pet Pigeon

Part 1: A new Pet

"Mother, Mother! Come quick," Andy
called from outside the screen door.
"You'll never guess what we have."

Mother came to the door. "What is it?"
she asked. She knew she could not guess.
It was hard to tell what the boys would
come up with next. Then she saw the
young pigeon in Andy's hand. "Oh, Andy, where did you get that?" she asked.

"Out in the barn," Andy said. "Since
we filled the haymow we don't have to
climb high to get to the pigeon nests. I
wanted to climb up to see if any of them
had eggs. Just before I got to a nest,
this pigeon flew out. It couldn't fly very
well, and landed on the hay. Daniel
caught it. It didn't even try to get away."

"What are you going to do with it?"
asked Mother. Then without waiting for
an answer, she asked another question.
"Where is Daniel now?"

"He went to the woodshed to get a basket. We're going to put the pigeon under a basket until we have a cage ready for it." The boys had everything planned out. "You know those rabbit cages Dad bought at a sale? We are going to fix one of those for the pigeon."

Mother touched the back of the frightened young bird. "Be very careful you don't hurt it," she said. "Poor little thing. Don't you feel sorry for it?"

"Why should we feel sorry for it?" asked Daniel. He came up the walk carrying a basket. "We are going to give it feed and water. We will take good care of it."

The boys put the pigeon under the basket. They put a heavy block on top of the basket so it would not blow away. Then they ran to get the cage ready. "I have always wanted a pet pigeon, and now we have one," Daniel said. "I wish we could catch another one, so we would have a pair. Then we could raise pigeons like Uncle Abe does."

Soon the cage was ready. The boys put their new pet into it. They gave it some corn meal and rolled oats that Mother had given to them. They put in a dish of fresh water, too. Then they ran to the barn to see if they could catch another pigeon. "If we get another one, this one will not be by itself," Daniel said.

The boys were disappointed. Not one of the other nests had any young pigeons in it. They had to be satisfied with just one pet pigeon.

That evening when Dad came home, the boys ran to tell him about their new pet. Dad went to look at the pigeon. "Did you see it eat?" he asked.

"No, I don't think it is hungry yet," Daniel said. "Maybe the mother pigeon fed it just before we caught it."

Dad looked a little doubtful, but he did not say much. He told the boys to be careful they did not hurt the pigeon. Then he went back to his work.

To the boy's delight, the baby pigeon ate when it got hungry. At first they fed it rolled oats and corn meal, but then they started giving it cows' feed.

The first few days the boys spent a lot of time by the pigeon's cage. The pigeon became very tame. It ate out of the boys' hands and cooed softly when one of them came near the cage. But the boys were careful they did not turn it loose. They were afraid it would fly away and never come back.

Part 2: A Happy Pet

Days went by. Soon the excitement of having a pet pigeon wore off. The boys made sure it had plenty of food and water, but they did not spend much time at the cage.

One morning Dad stood and looked at the pigeon. "I think it is time you turned this bird loose," he said.

"Turn it loose!" Andy said, sure he had not understood right. "We want to keep it."

"Pigeons are not made to be in cages," Dad said. "They like to fly around and be free. They like to look for their own food, and to sit on barn roofs."

"This pigeon has room to fly a little," Daniel said. He wanted to keep the pigeon as much as Andy did.

"How would you like to be in a little cage like this?" Dad asked.

"I couldn't even get into it," laughed Andy. "I'm bigger than the cage is."

"We'll find a cage that is the right size," Dad said. "The milk house might do, or maybe your bedroom. That would give you enough room to walk around and even run a little. Do you want to try it for a week and see if you like it?"

"A week!" The boys looked at each other. If Dad had said a day, that would have seemed too long. But a whole week! Surely Dad did not mean it.

"You are keeping this pigeon in its prison a lot longer than a week," Dad said.

"But we are nice to it. We give it plenty to eat, and fresh water every day," Daniel said.

"We'll give you plenty to eat, too," Dad said. "You'll get a tray of food three times a day, and more often if you want it."

Daniel walked away. He hated to lose his pet pigeon, but keeping her penned up like this made him feel sad. Later that day he and Andy were standing beside the cage, talking things over. "Let's turn it out," Andy said. "Maybe it won't be able to fly, then we can keep it. Remember, it couldn't fly right when we got it."

"I know, but it was too young then," Daniel said.

"But we don't know if it can fly or not," Andy said. "It hasn't had a chance to really try out its wings."

"All right," Daniel agreed. He opened the cage and reached into it. "I think we should take it up into the barn. It might get lost if we turn it loose out here."

The boys ran to the barn and climbed into the hayloft. Daniel opened his hand and stood still. Nothing happened. The pigeon just sat on Daniel's hand and cooed.

"It doesn't know it is loose," Andy whispered.

Then the pigeon hopped a few steps. It flew a little ways and landed on the hay. The boys stood watching. Andy could not wait any longer to find out if the pigeon could fly. He clapped his hands and said, "Shoo! Shoo!"

The pigeon spread out its wings and flew. Up and up and up! It sat on a high beam and cooed softly. Then it flew again. It looked as if it could hardly believe that it was really free.

The pigeon found the open barn door and flew out. The boys followed, feeling very excited. There, on the very top of the barn roof, sat their pet. The sun was shining on its blue feathers.

"It's pretty," Andy whispered. "It looks prettier now than it ever did in the cage."

"It looks happier, too," Daniel said.
"It is happier, too. It is free to fly
around and do the things other pigeons
do." And when he took time to think
about it, he discovered that he felt much
happier himself.

Erma's Secret

Part 1: Great Plans

It was Wednesday morning at Maple Grove School. The second and third-grade girls were standing in a corner of the basement. They were listening to Erma Mast's exciting plans. She was the oldest girl in the lower-grade room, so the others often looked to her as their leader.

"Let's have a food roll for Teacher Anna," Erma was saying. "You know, someone blows a whistle, then we all roll something toward her desk."

"I remember when we had one for our teacher when I was in the first grade," said Ada Kauffman. She was in the third grade, too.

"We didn't have one last year," Erma went on. "That means we have to explain to the first and second graders what it is and what they are supposed to do."

Erma gave the other girls a stern look. "The first thing to remember is don't tell. If the teacher finds out about it, it won't be any fun at all."

The girls nodded. They were sure they could keep a secret. It was the first graders they were worried about. "What about the little girls?" one of them asked. "Do you think they can keep a secret?"

"We won't tell them until last recess," Erma said. She had everything planned out. "That won't give them much time to tell. But the girl I am worried about is Verna Miller. She can't keep a secret, even if she is in the second grade."

"I don't think Verna will tell," Freda Troyer said. Verna was her best friend.

"Don't you remember what she did the time we wanted to surprise Teacher Anna by cleaning the classroom?" asked Erma. "She said, 'Teacher, we are going to surprise you.'"

"Yes, but that was a long time ago and she didn't know better," Freda said. "I'm sure she won't tell this time. We have to make sure she understands that she isn't supposed to tell."

"All right, we'll have to tell her. But if she doesn't keep the secret, we aren't going to play with her the rest of the year," Erma said, sounding very stern.

The door opened and another group of children came in. Verna was among them, along with a few of the second and third-grade girls.

"Verna, Mary, Susan, and Linda, come here," Erma said. "The rest of you have to go upstairs." Then seeing the hurt looks on some of the little girls' faces, she added, "We'll tell you our secret later on."

The little girls had to be satisfied with
that. They went upstairs. They were
used to doing what Erma told them to do.

Verna and the other girls were told
about the food roll. Erma did most of the
talking, especially when it came to telling the others not to say a word about it
to anyone.

"Don't say, 'We have a secret,' or
something like that," she said. She
looked right at Verna when she talked.
"If you say one word about it, we are going to be so cross, we won't play with you
the rest of the year."

"We won't tell," all the girls promised.
None of them wanted to be without friends
the rest of the year.

The bell rang and the children went up-stairs. Erma did not smile when she saw Teacher Anna, and she watched the other girls carefully. She saw that Verna had a funny smile on her face. She gave her a stern look. "I hope she doesn't tell, but I am afraid she will," she thought to her-self.

At recess the girls rushed around Erma. "Teacher Anna didn't guess the secret," Verna said excitedly.

"Well, we can't stand around here and whisper like this, or she will guess," Erma said, sounding a little cross. "Don't say another word about it until we tell the first graders at last recess."

Part 2: The Secret Is Out

As soon as the girls had eaten that day, they went outside. They wanted to talk about the secret, but Erma wouldn't let them. "Shhh! Teacher Anna's going to come out and hear you," she said sternly.

They had just started to play when Erma
saw that Verna wasn't on the playground.
She decided to check up on her. "I'm not
playing," she called to the others. "I
need a drink."

Walking softly, Erma opened the classroom door and peeped in. Verna was still
sitting at her desk, eating a piece of pie.
The only other children in the room were
first graders. They were still eating, too.

"Do you know what?" Erma heard
Verna say. She was too far away to hear
everything she said, but she heard a few
of the words. "We are going to —" Erma
didn't hear the rest of it, but she heard
Teacher Anna's surprised voice say,
"Really! That sounds like fun!"

Erma turned around and went outside.
Her heart was beating fast with anger and
disappointment. Why had they trusted
Verna with their secret? Now all the fun
was over and they could not have the food

roll. What was the use of having it when Teacher Anna knew about it? It was supposed to have been a surprise.

Erma called the other girls together. "Verna told the teacher," she said, sounding very angry. "I heard her."

The girls were just as upset as Erma was. "Are you sure?" asked Freda.

"Of course, I'm sure," Erma snapped. "I heard her with my own two ears. 'Teacher, do you know what we are going to do tomorrow?'" Erma made her voice sound funny, even if she was cross. "Teacher Anna said, 'Really! That sounds like fun.'"

Just then the schoolhouse door opened and Verna came out. "What are you playing?" she asked, sounding happy and eager to play.

The girls gave her stern looks. "What do you care what we are playing?" Erma asked crossly. "You aren't going to help."

"B—but why not?" asked Verna, looking hurt and surprised.

"Because you told. That's why. You told Teacher Anna about the food roll." Erma's voice was unkind.

41

"I did not," Verna said. She looked from one girl to the other. Then she repeated. "I did not."

"Yes, you did. I heard you. And you'd better not lie about it either, because that won't help. We're not going to play with you. Not ever for the rest of this year." Erma turned and started to walk away.

Verna burst into tears. Just then Teacher Anna came out the door. "Why, Verna, what's wrong?" she asked. "Did you get hurt?"

Verna shook her head. "They s-say I may not play with them," she sobbed.

"Why not?" Now it was Teacher Anna's turn to look stern. "Who said so?"

"Erma did," said Freda.

"Erma, come here," called the teacher.

Erma came, dragging her feet. She was almost in tears herself.

"Why did you say Verna may not play with you?" asked Teacher Anna.

"Because she told you our secret. We said this morning that anyone who tells you about the food roll we want to have tomorrow may not play with us the rest of the year. And now Verna has told."

A look of surprise came over Teacher Anna's face. It seemed as if she did not know whether to smile or to frown. At last she said, "No, Verna did not tell me a word about the secret. But I am afraid someone else did."

"Who?" demanded Erma, but then she knew. She had told the secret herself. "But I thought — I thought I heard her," she said.

Teacher Anna shook her head. "She did not tell me about the food roll. She told me that her family was going to Uncle Bens for supper tomorrow night. Maybe that is what you heard."

Erma hung her head. Everything was very still. No one said a word. At last Teacher Anna said, "Whose plan was it to punish the girl who tells by not playing with her the rest of the year?"

"Erma's," answered one of the girls.

Erma felt a hand on her shoulder. "That is not being forgiving," Teacher Anna said softly. "Do you want the other girls to be so unforgiving to you now?"

Erma shook her head.

Of course you don't," Teacher Anna said. "I think we can all learn something from this. When Jesus was on earth, he tried to teach the people to forgive one another. We still need to learn to do the same lesson. Forgive, and you shall be forgiven."

Teacher Anna looked around at the other girls. "Shall we forgive Erma for telling the secret, and go on being friends?" she asked. "Then surely she will do the same for the rest of you if you ever do anything that spoils her fun."

"Yes, yes," said all the girls.

"Good!" said the teacher. "Now, let's start playing."

Slowly Erma went over to the base to start playing. She no longer felt like the biggest girl in her room. She was no longer the other girls' leader, excited about her own wonderful plans. She felt small and humble and ashamed. Her friends had forgiven her, even when she had been so unforgiving.

Erma knew there was only one way in which she could thank her friends for be-ing kind and forgiving. That was by treating them the same way whenever they did something she did not like.

Luke 6:37

Forgive and ye shall be forgiven.

The Red Airplane

Rudy Mast was in the shop, making an
airplane. His older brother, Ray, had
made one. Rudy had looked it over carefully and decided he could make one, too.

First Rudy sawed off a board about a
foot long. Then he cut another piece
eight inches long. He nailed it across the
first piece. His airplane had front wings.
Next he cut a shorter piece and nailed it
across the back. Now his airplane had
hind wings, too.

The airplane was ready to fly. Rudy
was pleased with it. He held it high and
walked around, making a roaring sound.
The plane dived, then with a louder roar,
it climbed higher again.

The airplane took short turns and nearly
stood on end. Then it swooped low, just
like the sprayer planes Rudy had watched
when they sprayed the neighbor's hay
fields. Finally it made a perfect landing
on the workbench. Rudy turned the plane

around and made it take off again. He
could hardly believe he had made this
wonderful airplane all by himself.

Then Rudy saw a can of red paint on the
workbench. "Say, this is just what I
need," he thought. He put the plane
down, not even taking time to make it
land right. He looked around for something to open the can. Above the workbench were some tools. Rudy saw a
screwdriver. That was just the tool he
needed.

47

Rudy opened the can and looked thoughtfully into it. There was plenty of paint to coat his plane. That wasn't the problem. The problem was, he wasn't sure if Dad and Mom wanted him to use it. He had never been allowed to paint anything before, but he was sure he knew how. And it would take such a little bit of paint. He decided to go ahead and do it.

Rudy looked around for a brush, but
there was none in sight. Then he remembered that Dad kept the brushes in the
other part of the shop. He ran and got
one that was just the right size.

All the while Rudy was painting, he
kept thinking how nice his airplane would
look. It was fun, painting the plane.
Rudy decided that was even more fun
than making it.

Rudy got some paint on his fingers, but
he didn't care. He put the lid back on
the can and lay the brush carefully on the
top. Then he wiped his fingers on the
front of his pants. "Now, if it would
only dry fast," he thought, looking at his
plane. "I can hardly wait to show it to
Ray."

Several minutes passed. Rudy touched
the plane with the tip of his finger. It
was still as wet as it had been when he
had finished painting it. He sighed.
How long was it going to take?

Rudy walked around in the shop, won-dering what he could do to pass the time. He was just inside the back door when he heard footsteps on the porch outside the front door. Through the window in the door, he saw Mother. She had a hoe in her hand, which she wanted to sharpen.

Now that Rudy stopped to think about it, he was sure Mother would not be pleased with him. He went out the back door and ran toward the barn as fast as he could go. How he hoped Mother was not looking out the window.

Rudy went into the barn and tried to act busy. Before he had even started working, he heard Mother's voice. "Ru-dy! Rudy! Where are you?"

Rudy walked to the barn door. "Out here," he answered. "What do you want?"

"Come here," Mother said. She stood outside the door of the shop, waiting for him. There was nothing Rudy could do but go.

When Rudy got to the shop, Mother pointed to the red airplane. "Did you do that?"

Almost before Rudy knew what he was doing, he shook his head. "No, I didn't."

"Then who did?" Mother asked.

"I don't know," Rudy answered. "Maybe it was Ray. He made an airplane the other day." His heart was beating fast and his hands were deep in his pockets. He was very careful to leave them there.

Mother looked thoughtfully at Rudy. "Are you sure it wasn't you?"

"Yes, I'm sure," Rudy said. His voice shook so that he could hardly say it.

"Stay right here until I come back," Mother said. She turned and walked out of the shop. Rudy knew she was going to find Ray.

Rudy was really afraid now. He could not remember ever having told such a big lie before. He could not understand why he had done it now. But by thinking it over, he knew why. He was afraid Mother would be displeased with him. He had thought he could get out of being punished by telling a lie. But he knew now that he had made things worse by lying. There was no doubt about it; he would be sure to get a punishment.

Mother came back. Rudy stood looking at the floor. He could not make himself look at Mother.

Mother took Rudy by the shoulder and turned him around. Now the light from the window was shining on his pants. "Let me see your hands," she said.

Slowly Rudy took them out of his pockets. He hoped the red paint had disappeared somehow, but of course it hadn't. It was still there, as bright and red as ever.

"Rudy, why did you lie to me?" Mother asked, sounding very sad.

Rudy swallowed hard. He could not say a word.

"If you had told me the truth, I could have told you not to do it again and let you off," Mother said. "See what a mess you made on Dad's workbench. And leaving a brush out like this without cleaning it makes it hard and stiff so that it can't be used again. But all that is not nearly as bad as telling a lie."

Rudy stood looking at the floor. "I'm s-sorry," he said. "I'm v-very s-sorry."

"I believe you," Mother said. "But to help you remember to always tell the truth, no matter what you have done, I will have to punish you."

Mother went to the willow tree behind the shop to get a switch. It did not take her long to find one. Even before Rudy had taken his punishment, he had made up his mind. He would always try to tell the truth after this. He had found out that even though the truth sometimes hurts, telling a lie hurts even more.

SPRINGTIME

I went in search of spring one day;
I looked on hill and dale;
I found a robin redbreast's nest,
And crossed a chipmonk's trail.

I peeked into a shady glen,
And found a violet;
I heard a wren sing in the tree—
A song I'll not forget.

I sniffed the blossoms on the trees;
I trampled through the rain;
I saw a rainbow in the sky;
I wandered down a lane.

I found the promise of new life
Wherever I had trod;
Some folks may call it springtime—
But I will call it God.

Unit Two:

Lessons to Learn

Verna's Vacation

Part 1: Too Many People

Verna stared at the stack of dishes on the sink. She sighed. "Oh, so many dishes!" She was the oldest girl in the family, and there was always so much work to be done.

It might not have been so bad if half of the children had been girls. But that is not the way it was. Verna had only one sister. Her name was Mary and she was two years younger than Verna. All the other children were boys.

"When Freda washes dishes, she only needs to wash five plates, five glasses, and five of everything else," Verna said. "That's not even half as many as we have to wash."

"Freda has only half as many brothers as you do, and no sister," Mom said. "I know we have lots of dishes, but let's just be thankful we have something to put

into them. There are people who don't
need to wash dishes, because they don't
have enough food to eat."

Verna didn't answer. Mom often talked
about the people who didn't have much to
eat, especially when the children grumbled about having to work so hard.

Verna and Mary took turns to wash the dishes. But even when Verna didn't have to wash dishes, there was always something else to do. One thing they had to do several times a day was pick up the toys and sweep the floor. Verna didn't mind doing this, but she didn't like to do it so often. She could pick up all the toys and sweep the floor in the morning, and when she came home in the afternoon the toys were scattered all over the house again. Mom usually told the boys to help pick them up, but there were always some toys under the furniture and in the corners that they missed.

Verna didn't think it was fun, being the oldest girl in such a big family. It meant she had to work all the time.

Then something happened that gave Verna an unexpected vacation. Grandma, who lived in another state, became ill. Dad and Mom and part of the family were going to visit her. Only the school children were going to stay at home. They were not going to stay by themselves. Aunt Katie was coming to stay with them.

Verna was almost as excited about staying at home as the others were about going. "There will only be five people here while you are gone," she said. "It won't take long to wash the dishes, and the toys won't be scattered every day. I'm sure I'm not going to be as busy as I usually am."

The ones who were going away left early one morning before Verna was up. It was fun to set the table for only five people. It was even more fun to wash the dishes. "There are only a few," she thought happily. She could not believe how fast she got them done.

It was Saturday. Verna was extra careful with the cleaning that day, because she knew things would stay nice and neat. With none of the little boys at home, the work was soon done. Then she and Mary had the rest of the day off to do what they wanted to do.

The next day the girls went to church with Aunt Katie. It didn't seem right, being in church without Dad and Mom, but Verna didn't mind it much. That evening they went away for supper, so the time did not seem long. Then they came home and got ready to go to bed. Verna was tired and soon fell asleep. There was a smile on her face as she thought of how much fun it was to have such a small family.

Part 2: A Long Week

The first time Verna really missed the rest of the family was on Monday afternoon. The children had just come home from school. Aunt Katie had to go away that day, so the house was empty and cold. Eli, the oldest boy who was at home, soon had a fire going in the stove. But things still didn't seem right.

The house was so empty and still that it gave Verna a funny feeling. She thought maybe she was getting sick, but when she got busy with her chores, the funny feeling went away. Soon Aunt Katie came home and started supper. That evening Verna didn't enjoy washing the dishes, even if there were only a few.

"Is it tomorrow that Daddy and Mom are coming home?" asked Mary. She was a first grader and the youngest one at home.

"No, not tomorrow," Aunt Katie answered. "This is Monday, then it will be Tuesday, then Wednesday, then Thursday. They plan to come home on Thursday."

"Oh, so long," Mary said. She went to the calendar to count the days. Verna went over to make sure she counted right. "Why, they are coming home on Freeman's birthday!" she exclaimed. It seemed like such a long time since she had seen her youngest brother. "He will be two then."

"I can hardly wait until they come home," Mary said.

Aunt Katie smiled. "Maybe we can bake some cookies one evening as a surprise for them," she said.

"Oh, yes! Let's," the girls said.

The next two days dragged slowly by. When Verna was in school she almost forgot that Daddy and Mom and five of her brothers weren't at home. But when she came home, she could not forget. She found the house as neat and clean as it had been in the morning, but she did not enjoy having it like that. It seemed too big and quiet and different. Of course, Aunt Katie was there, but she didn't make much noise, and she didn't scatter the toys on the floor.

The evenings seemed long. Verna and Mary always carried wood. Usually there were little boys to talk to and play with as they worked. Now with no one to follow them around, the work went much faster. Verna had always thought she would like to play if she had the time. Now, to her surprise, she discovered that she didn't even feel like playing.

Aunt Katie tried to keep the children busy. One evening they played a game after supper. One evening they made cookies. They always had a story before they went to bed. They always sang the new song they were learning. But the evening were still very long.

At last it was Wednesday evening. "To-morrow the others will come home," Mary said. "Then we will have a big family again."

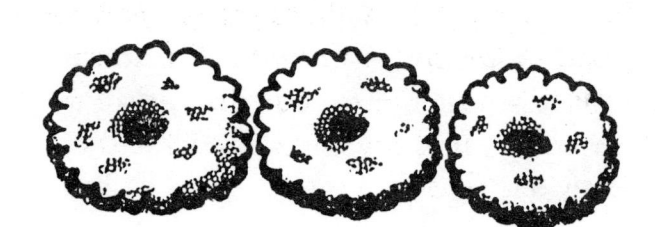

"Then you will have many dishes to wash," reminded Aunt Katie.

"I don't care. I'm still glad they are coming home," Mary said.

"So am I," Verna added.

"Of course you are," smiled Aunt Katie. "You will be glad to see them, and they will be just as glad to see you."

The next day at school Verna couldn't keep her mind on her lessons. "Today... today...today!" her heart sang. "I hope they will be there when we get home."

They were. Verna and Mary burst into the house that afternoon. It was no longer quiet and empty. It wasn't neat either, with all the suitcases and boxes standing

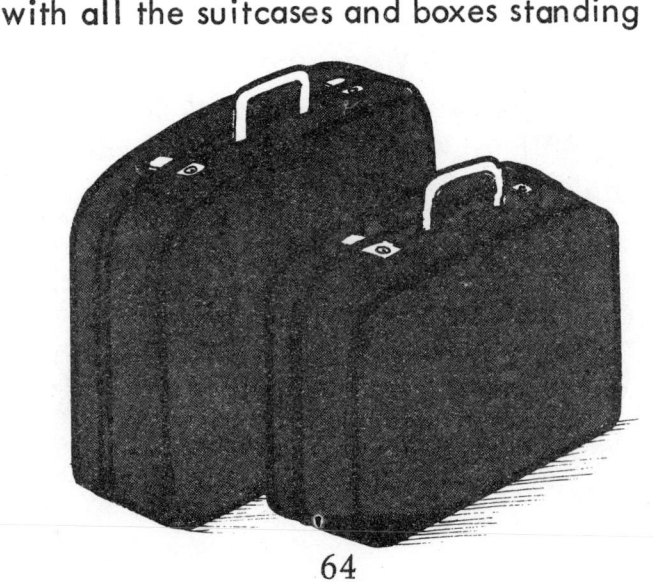

around. But Verna didn't mind. She didn't even seem to notice them.

She did notice, however, that Daddy and Mom were home. So were the two big boys and the three little boys. She was so busy talking with them that she did not notice that they had already found the toy box and had scattered the toys all over the house.

The ones who had been away had much to tell about their trip. But the ones at home had things to tell, too. The neighbors had a new baby. The chores had gone just fine, and there were some little pigs in the barn that had not been there when they had left. Everyone was so busy talking that they almost didn't have time to do the chores that evening. But finally they were done, and then they sat down at the supper table and talked some more.

After supper Verna washed the dishes. She did not mind that her vacation was over, and that she had eleven plates, eleven glasses, and eleven of everything else to wash. She had discovered that their family wasn't too big after all. It was just the right size.

An Eraser and a Ruler

Part 1: Easy Work for Leroy

Leroy sat in his seat and stared at his friend, Daniel, who sat across the aisle. Daniel still had his reading workbook out and was trying to do his lesson. Leroy had finished his a long time ago. "I can't understand why he doesn't hurry up and finish his work," Leroy thought. "It isn't hard."

Just then Daniel held up his hand, which meant he wanted Teacher Linda to come and help him. Leroy leaned across the aisle to see which question Daniel couldn't get. Daniel saw him and pointed to the fourth one.

"That's easy," Leroy whispered. He didn't really say the words, because they weren't suppose to whisper. He just moved his lips, but Daniel understood him all the same.

Teacher Linda came down the aisle. "Yes, Daniel, what can I do for you?" she asked.

"I can't get this one," Daniel said, pointing to the fourth question.

"Did you see if you can find the answer in your reading book?" the teacher asked.

Daniel nodded.

"Read the question," Teacher Linda said.

Leroy listened as Daniel tried to read the question. He didn't know all the words. "No wonder he can't get the answer. He can't even read the question," Leroy thought, laughing to himself.

Teacher Linda helped Daniel find the answer in his reading book. Then she looked at Leroy. "Is your work all finished?" she asked.

Leroy nodded. He felt pleased with himself. "It didn't take me long to do that page," he said. "The questions were all very easy."

"Get out your spelling book and write sentences with the new words," Teacher Linda said. "That will give you something to do."

Leroy got out his spelling book and set to work. "I am going to see if I can finish these sentences before Daniel is done with his reading workbook," he thought.

Leroy and Daniel were the only second graders at Hilltop School. It was not hard for Leroy to keep up with his work. It was easy for him to learn something new. But with Daniel it was different. The work was all hard for him. It took him a long time to do anything. Often he had to do it over because he had not

done it right. Then the teacher had to
give Leroy extra work to keep him busy
until Daniel was ready for the next lesson.
Even then Leroy often sat with nothing to
do.

One day Leroy discovered how much
fun it was to read library books. At first
he read little books that did not take long.
Then he started to read bigger books. He
liked the stories he found in the books.
They were very interesting and exciting.

Part 2: Trouble for Leroy

Now that Leroy enjoyed reading library
books, he had another reason for working
fast. Up until now he had worked fast so
he could get done before Daniel did. But
now he worked fast so he had more time
to read his books.

One morning Teacher Linda took the
second-grade workbooks to her desk to
check them at recess. After recess Leroy
saw her coming down the aisle. She was

carrying two workbooks and her big green eraser. "Goody. Daniel will have to do his lesson over," Leroy thought. "That will give me time to read my book."

But it wasn't Daniel who had to do his work over that morning. It was Leroy. "You will have to do this page over," she said, looking down at him.

"Why?" asked Leroy. It was just a page of questions they had to answer. He was sure he had answered them right.

"You were too careless with your work," Teacher Linda said. "Did you read your answers after you had written them down?"

Leroy shook his head.

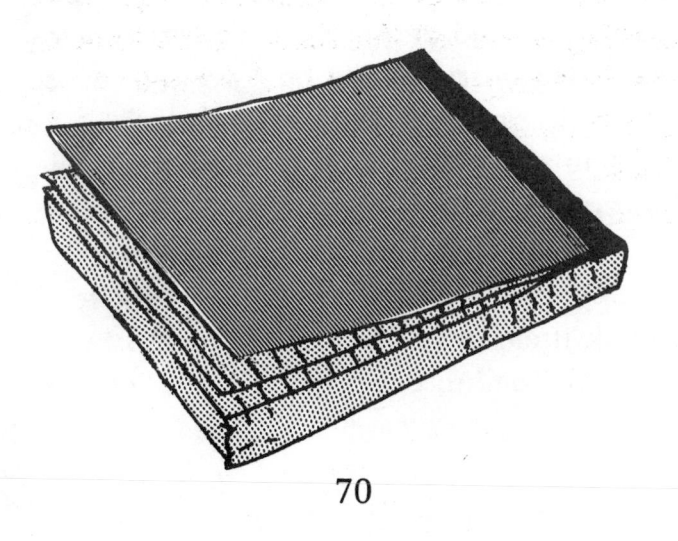

"Read the first answer out loud, please," the teacher said.

Leroy started to read. "But truck — ." He stopped and laughed a little. "I skipped a word."

"Read the second answer, please." Teacher Linda did not laugh. She didn't even smile.

This time Leroy read it quickly to himself. He saw that he had skipped some words there, too. He looked helplessly at his teacher.

"Your sentences don't sound right, do they?" Teacher Linda said. She started to erase his work for him. "And that is not all," she said, talking in a low voice. "Look at your handwriting. It is getting worse all the time. Let's look at the first pages you did in this book." She flipped back to the first part of the book. Leroy saw what she was talking about. He had written very neatly then.

Back and forth went the teacher's big eraser — back and forth, back and forth. Then the whole page was blank and Leroy had to start over. He felt warm. He could not believe that this was really happening to him. It was Daniel who had to do his work over. Leroy had often watched the teacher's eraser fly back and forth over Daniel's page. But he had never thought it would happen to him. He swallowed hard and tried to hold back his tears.

Teacher Linda brushed away the bits of eraser that had rubbed off. "I want you to do the whole page over," she said. "Don't hurry. Do your work carefully and neatly. Read your answers to your-self to make sure you did not skip any words." She smiled down at Leroy. "Maybe I had better take your library book to my desk until you have done this page right."

Leroy quickly handed her his library book. It was a long time before he looked up from his work. He expected all the children to be watching him, but they weren't. They were busy with their work.

"Don't hurry. Do your work carefully and neatly." That's what the teacher had said. Leroy tried, but he was in the habit of working fast and carelessly. He found it hard to make his letters look right. He wrote and erased, and wrote again. The longer he worked, the worse his page looked.

At last Leroy was finished. He read each sentence to make sure the words were all there. He did not like the way his page looked. He was sure the teacher would not be pleased with the black marks his eraser had made.

"Are you finished?" asked Teacher Linda, stopping at his desk to look at his work.

Leroy felt his face get red. Would the teacher be pleased with his work this time?

She did not seem to see the black marks at all. "That is much better," she said. "Now let's see if you can do just as well next time."

The next time the second graders were asked to do a page in their workbook, Leroy worked carefully. The teacher praised him when she checked his work. "Keep up the good work, Leroy," she said. "You can do your work neatly if you try."

For a while all went well. Then Leroy became careless again. Teacher Linda noticed it and reminded him to be more careful. Two days later she made him do a page over again. Leroy felt badly about it, but not as badly as he had the first time.

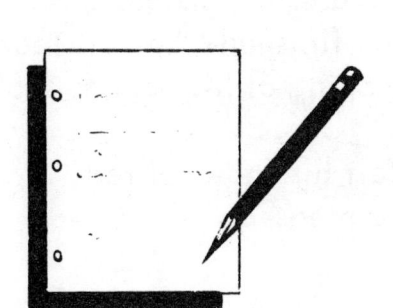

Then one day Teacher Linda made him copy his spelling sentences over again. When it was time for recess, he wasn't quite finished. The teacher asked him to finish before he went out to play.

Leroy wrote fast. His mind was only on one thing — getting done so he could go out to play. He wrote the last word, threw down his pencil, and took the paper up to the teacher's desk.

"Are you finished? " asked Teacher Linda with a smile.

Leroy didn't feel like smiling back. He nodded. He was halfway across the room on his way out when Linda called him back. "I'm sorry, Leroy, but you are not going out yet. Look at the last three sentences. They are not written a bit better than they were the first time. You will have to write them again."

Leroy was cross — just plain cross. He couldn't do anything good enough to please the teacher. She was fussy. That was the problem, and not his handwriting.

If Teacher Linda saw that Leroy was cross, she did not say a word about it. She just explained to him that some children had to work hard to get their lessons done on time. Others had to work hard to learn something new. Still others had to work hard to be neat.

Leroy was like that, the teacher said. She knew he could do very neat work when he tried to. But there were times when he was in too much of a hurry to do his best. That was why she asked him to do his work over — to remind him to always do his best.

Leroy cried a little, but he copied the last three sentences over. He did the best he could, but that wasn't very good. His hands were shaking. But Teacher Linda seemed to understand. "That's pretty good," she said when he was finished. She smiled at him. "Do you think you can remember to do your best the first time from now on?"

Leroy looked at the floor and shrugged his shoulders.

"You'll try, won't you?" Teacher Linda reached out and patted his shoulder.

Leroy smiled and raced out to the playground. Even though he didn't have much time left to play, he was not cross. It was hard to stay cross with a teacher like Linda.

Part 3: Another Reminder

The weeks went on, one after the other. For a while Leroy did well in his work. Then he grew careless again. Soon he had to do his work over. The teacher's green eraser got smaller and smaller. She talked to Leroy again and again about doing his work carefully and neatly. Each time she talked to him, he did better for a few days. Then he got careless again.

One day the second graders had a page of questions to answer in their workbook. Leroy made a face at the page before he started. It wasn't that he thought the questions were hard. He just didn't want

to do them. He was reading a book about
a fawn who had lost its mother. The mother was dead, but the fawn didn't know
it yet. He wanted to read the next chap-
ter to see what would happen to the fawn.
But he knew he had to do his reading
work first.

Leroy answered the questions. He did
not need to use his reading book once.
He knew all the answers, and it did not
take him long to write them down. He
forgot all about being careful. He forgot
all about reading his sentences to see if
they sounded right. He remembered only
one thing. He wanted to finish quickly
so he could go back to his library book.

That evening Teacher Linda asked for the second-grade workbooks. Leroy felt a little guilty about handing his book in. He was almost sure he would have to do his page over. "Oh, well, I have finished my library book now," he thought. "I will have time to do it over tomorrow."

The next day Leroy forgot all about his reading workbook until it was time for recess. Then Teacher Linda asked him to stay in. He made a face that made some of the other boys laugh. He wasn't really worried about having to stay in. It had happened so often the last while that he was used to it.

When all the other children had gone out to play, Teacher Linda came down the aisle to Leroy's seat. She was carrying his workbook, her eraser, and a wooden ruler. Instead of starting to talk like Leroy expected her to, she just stood and looked at Leroy. At last she said, "Leroy, did you do your best on this workbook page yesterday?"

Leroy shook his head.

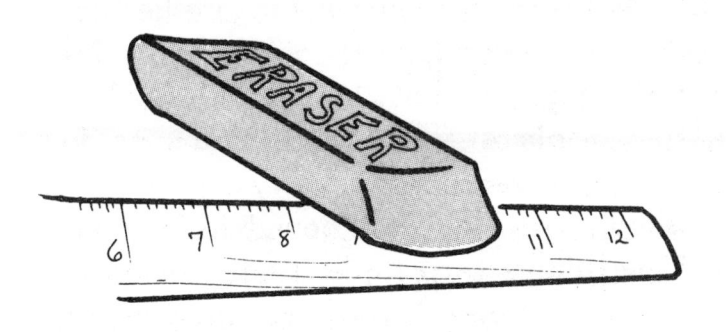

"You hurried with your work, didn't you?" Teacher Linda asked, opening the book to the right page. She showed him his work. There was not one sentence that was written right. Some of the writing was done so carelessly that she could not read it. He had many capital letters where he did not need them, and many small letters where he needed capitals.

Teacher Linda set to work. She erased all the work Leroy had done the day before. She talked to Leroy, explaining once again that he had to do his best. She said he had to do his best without having to be reminded all the time.

Then Leroy knew why Teacher Linda had brought her ruler to his desk. He had been careless too often. He did not care if he had to do his work over. He did not care if he had to stay in. The reminders Teacher Linda had given him no longer helped. She was going to give him a different kind of reminder this time.

When Leroy's page was blank, the teacher put down her eraser and picked up the ruler. She used it on Leroy's hand, making it hurt enough that he would remember it for a long time.

Leroy, who had tears in his eyes before the punishment, could hardly stop sobbing now. Teacher Linda rubbed his hand gently and talked to him. "I know it hurts, and I'm sorry I had to do this to you," she said. "But I want to help you remember to always do your best."

Leroy wiped the tears from his eyes. When the other children came in a few minutes later, he was hard at work. He wrote his sentences carefully. Then he read them to make sure they sounded right. He had made up his mind to always do his best. He did not want Teacher Linda to remind him with her ruler again.

Two Heavy Pennies

Part 1: The Ice Cream Bar

Lester Miller went to a large school. It had eight classrooms and three playrooms. It had a kitchen where lunch was made for the children.

Some of the children bought their lunch every day. But Lester did not. He carried his lunch to school in a dinner bucket. He liked the lunches his mother fixed for him. He often had sandwiches and fruit and milk for lunch. Sometimes he had a cookie or a piece of pie. He always had plenty to eat.

In one corner of the room where the children sat to eat was an ice cream counter. It had glass doors. Lester liked to look in through the glass doors. He could see ice cream bars, ice cream cups, and ice cream sandwiches. How good they all looked!

An ice cream bar cost six cents. How Lester wished he had six cents to buy an ice cream bar. His friend, David, carried his lunch to school, too. But nearly every day he had money in his pocket to buy ice cream.

One day Lester needed a pencil. His father gave him a dime. "You will get four cents back," Dad said. "Keep them until you need another pencil. Then I will give you two cents more, and you will have enough money to buy your next pencil."

Lester did as he was told. He bought the pencil. He put the four cents into a box he had in his desk. "Four cents," he thought. "I wish I had two cents more. Then I could buy an ice cream bar."

Lester's conscience started to speak to him. "Oh, no, not an ice cream bar," it said. "Dad would not like that. He told you to keep the money until you need another pencil. It would be wrong to buy ice cream with it."

There was another voice inside of Lester. Sometimes it seemed louder than the voice of his conscience. "Dad will forget those four pennies," it said. "Spend them for ice cream. Just think how good that would taste."

But Lester could not buy an ice cream bar. How could he, when he needed six cents and had only four? He would just have to forget it. He did not have enough money to buy himself a treat.

One day Lester was busy with his work. The lead in his pencil broke. He wanted to use his other pencil, but it was broken, too. He held up his hand. "I need a pencil," he told the teacher.

"Go up to my desk and get one," the teacher said. "They are in the top drawer."

Lester went up to the desk. Slowly he opened the drawer and got a pencil. He chose one with a good, sharp point. The teacher kept them there for the children who needed them. Lester knew he had to sharpen his pencil at recess, and then put this one back.

Lester was just about ready to close the drawer when he saw something — four pennies! For a little while he wondered if they were his pennies, but he knew they were not. He had seen his only a few minutes ago. These were four other pennies. If only he had two of them! Then he could buy an ice cream bar.

Once again Lester's conscience warned
him. "No, Lester, no," it said. "That
would be stealing, and stealing is sin.
Don't do it." His face got red and his
heart beat fast. He felt as if he had already done something he shouldn't have.
He quickly closed the drawer and went to
his seat.

Lester tried to forget the four pennies
in the teacher's drawer, but he couldn't.
"Two pennies is not very much money.
Teacher would never miss them," he
thought. But his conscience did not
agree. "Two pennies may not be much
money, but stealing them would still be
a sin," it reminded him.

All that evening Lester thought about
the pennies. He thought about the treat
he could buy if he had them. He thought

86

how nice it would be if he could walk around eating an ice cream bar, like so many of the other children did.

The next day at first recess the children were outside playing. "This is my chance," Lester thought. He went into the schoolhouse. He took a book out of his desk and made it look as if he were hunting for something.

No one else was in the room. Lester went to the teacher's desk and opened the drawer. Yes, the pennies were still there. He reached out and was just ready to touch them when a door banged. Lester slammed the drawer shut and ran back to his seat. His heart beat rapidly. What if someone had caught him?

No one came into Lester's room. Soon he was back at the teacher's desk again. This time he got the two pennies he wanted. He put them into his pocket and hurried outside. "I have them, and no one saw me!" he told himself over and over. But he did not feel as happy about it as he had expected to. In fact, he did not feel happy at all. He felt guilty and afraid. "What if the teacher opens the drawer and sees that the pennies are gone?" he thought.

But the teacher did not open the drawer. Everything went on just like usual, except that Lester's heart beat much too fast. When the children went down to the big room to eat, Lester took his six pennies along. He could not believe how heavy they felt in his pocket. Once they bumped together and made a loud noise. He quickly put his hand over them and held them tightly. He was afraid someone would hear his pennies and ask where he got them.

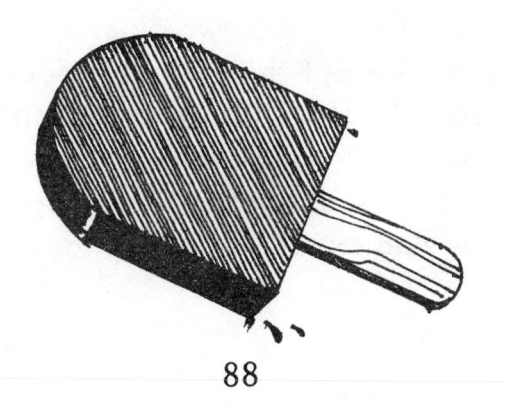

After they had eaten their lunch, Lester stood up. "I think I'll buy an ice cream bar today," he said to his friend, Andy. He tried to make it sound as if he did it every day.

Andy looked surprised. "Do you have money to buy ice cream?" he asked.

"Yes, my mother gave it to me," Lester said, and then he stopped quickly. He had told a lie. He had not meant to tell a lie, but it had just popped out. What would Andy think of him now?

But Andy did not know that Lester had lied to him. "I wish I had money to buy ice cream," he said. "But my mother says we have to save our money to pay for other things."

Lester knew Andy's parents did not have much money. They lived in an old house. They had to be careful what they bought, or they did not have enough money to pay for it. But he did not have much time to think about that now. He was on his way to buy a treat — the ice cream bar he had wanted for such a long while.

The ice cream bar was very cold. It should have tasted good, but it didn't. Lester didn't enjoy it a bit. He was afraid someone would see him eating it, and ask where he had gotten the money to pay for it. He was glad when the last bite was gone, and he was on his way to the playground.

All that day and the next Lester had an uneasy feeling. It seemed as if all the children looked at him in such a strange way. "I am just imagining things," he kept telling himself. "No one knows what I did. And besides, I did not do much. I only took two pennies. I didn't steal them; I just took them."

But Lester's conscience didn't give him any rest. "You stole the pennies," it said. "And even the four pennies you had in your desk were not to be spent on ice cream."

Part 2: A Silent Lie

Several days later the teacher stood in front of the classroom. "Children," she said, looking at them all as she spoke, "there were four pennies in my drawer several days ago, and now there are only two. Does anyone know what happened to the other two?"

The classroom was very still. Lester was sure someone would point at him and say, "He took them. I saw him eat an ice cream bar the other day." He was sure the teacher would hear his heart pound and see his guilty look.

"Does anyone know anything about it?" the teacher asked again.

The other children shook their heads, and Lester shook his, too. He felt hot all over, because he knew he was not being honest. He did know something about it.

"I am very sorry this has happened," the teacher said. "The pennies were not mine. They were Andy's. He was saving them to buy a pencil the next time he needs one. This morning he brought two more cents. When I wanted to give him the four pennies I was keeping for him, two of them were gone."

Lester felt worse than ever. He had not stolen from the teacher, but from Andy — his good friend Andy, whose parents did not have much money. Andy liked ice cream as much as anyone, but he never bought any. His family had to save money wherever they could.

Why had he ever done it? Oh, why had he? He knew what he would do. At recess he would go and tell the teacher what he had done. Then he would tell his parents, too. He would ask for two pennies to replace the ones he had stolen. Once Lester had made up his mind to do this, he felt a little better.

But when recess came, Lester changed his mind. "What will Andy think of me?" he thought. "What will the teacher do to me? Dad and Mom will be sure to give me a hard punishment." Recess passed, and Lester did not try to make his things right.

From then on Lester was very unhappy. His conscience gave him no rest. "You stole, and you lied," it kept reminding him.

"I didn't lie. I just didn't say any-thing," Lester tried to tell himself. But that did not help. He remembered the other lie he had told. He knew he had shaken his head when the teacher had asked if they knew anything about the missing pennies. That was the same as telling a lie.

Then something happened that brought a change to Lester's life. His family was going to move, then he would go to another school. Lester knew he would miss his friends, but in one way he was glad. They would be moving away from Andy and the other children he knew. Maybe that would help him forget about the two pennies he had taken.

But moving away did not help Lester forget. It was not that way at all. Instead, his conscience bothered him more and more. Sometimes it seemed as if those two pennies were still in his pocket, getting heavier and heavier all the time.

One Sunday in church, Lester sat listening to the preacher. He was telling about a man who had stolen some things and hidden them. He had buried them in his tent. No one had seen him steal. No one had seen him dig the hole to bury the things he had stolen. And yet God knew all the while that he had done it. The man had to die as his punishment.

"Often when we do something that is wrong, we lie about it, too," the preacher said. "Or if we don't lie, we pretend we don't know anything about it. That is the same as telling a lie."

Lester felt himself getting hot all over. He felt as badly as he had the day he had stolen the pennies. He felt the same as when he had not told the teacher the truth. He felt like he had so many times before, when his conscience reminded him that he had done wrong. It was not a good feeling. Lester knew he could not go on living with this guilty feeling.

When Lester got home from church that day, he told his parents what he had done. They were both very sorry about it, but they were glad he wanted to make things right.

95

"You thought you could run away from your guilty feeling," Dad said. "But when you moved, your conscience came with you to your new home. I hope you will listen to your conscience sooner after this. It will save you much trouble if you do."

Lester nodded. He knew very well what Dad was talking about. That evening he got out his paper and pencil and wrote a letter to his teacher. He put in a note for Andy, too, and sent him two pennies that he had taken out of his own bank. He was almost ready to seal the letter when he had another idea. He put in another nickel and a penny. "Use the other six cents to buy yourself a treat," he wrote to Andy. "This is a gift from me to show you how sorry I am. I hope you can forgive me."

When Lester went to bed that evening, he could hardly believe how good he felt. For the first time since he had taken those two pennies, he did not feel guilty and afraid. He went to sleep with a peaceful feeling in his heart. How good it felt!

Wilma Waits for Help

"Wilma, I want you and Susie to wash the dishes and sweep the floor this morning," Mom said when breakfast was over. "Please do it nicely, and don't fuss. When you are finished, you may play until I come back."

"Where are you going?" Wilma asked.

"Dad and I want to pick peas," Mom answered. "We have to be finished before noon, because a man is going to pick them up and take them to market."

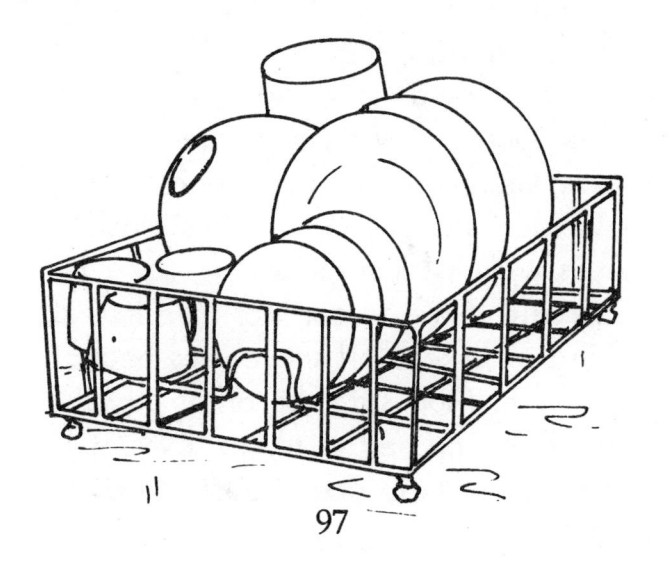

Wilma was glad Dad and Mom weren't going to pick strawberries, because then she and Susie would have to help. But peas were harder to pick. They didn't turn red when they were ripe, like strawberries did. And since they didn't turn red, the girls never knew which ones to pick.

"Come on, Susie," Wilma called. "Clear the table while I fix the dishwater."

Susie came to help, but she wasn't in a hurry. Slowly she started to stack the dishes.

"Hurry up, Susie," Wilma said, her voice barely louder than a whisper. "Let's do our work and then I'll make your doll a new dress. The sewing machine is open and Mom gave me some left-over material like our green dresses."

"Did Mom say you may?" Susie asked, her eyes wide with surprise.

"She said if we do our work we may do anything we like until she comes back."

"I thought Mom said the other day that you are not supposed to try to sew until she is ready to help you," Susie said.

Wilma did not answer right away.
"Y-yes, she said that," she said slowly.
"But then she helped me for awhile, and
I know how now. I'm not sure I could put
the thread on the sewing machine, but I
checked and it is on. The machine is all
ready to go. Let's hurry, so I can get
started."

Just then Mom came into the house to get some more baskets. Wilma felt a little uneasy about her plans. She was pretty sure that if she asked Mom, the answer would be, "No." Then she had an idea. "Mom, did you say if we wash the dishes and sweep the floors, we may do anything we want to until you come back?" she asked.

"Yes, but be sure you do your work first, and do it right," Mom said.

"See, we can do anything we want to," Wilma said to Susie, as soon as Mom was out the door. "Let's hurry with our work."

The girls hurried. They could work fast if they wanted to. Wilma washed the dishes and Susie dried them. Then Wilma swept the kitchen and Susie swept the living room. They were careful to do their work right, just as Mom had told them to. Soon the dishes were all put away and the floors were nice and clean. Then Wilma got out the material to make the doll's dress.

"Bring your doll, and also one of her dresses," Wilma said. "I have to measure to make sure it will be the right size."

Mom had helped Wilma make a dress for her doll one rainy day, so she knew a little about it. But when it came to doing it by herself, she wasn't at all sure of herself. But that didn't stop her. "It may not look exactly like the ones Mom makes, but it will be a dress," she thought.

"Snip! Snip! Snip!" went the scissors. Wilma cut out the dress and pinned it together, just like Mom did when she made a dress for one of the girls. At last the cutting and pinning were finished, and Wilma was ready to start sewing.

Wilma sat on the very edge of the chair. She had to, so her feet would reach the treadle. She was very careful to put both threads in back of the needle before she started. Mom had showed her how to do this. This was to keep the thread from knotting.

"Whirrr-r-r-r!" went the sewing machine. It did not run as smoothly as it did when Mom was sewing, but Wilma didn't mind. She was sewing — really sewing — all by herself.

"Won't Mom be surprised when she sees that your doll has a new dress," Wilma said happily.

"Maybe she'll scold you for sewing when she wasn't here to help you," Susie said.

"She said we may do whatever we want to," Wilma reminded her sister.

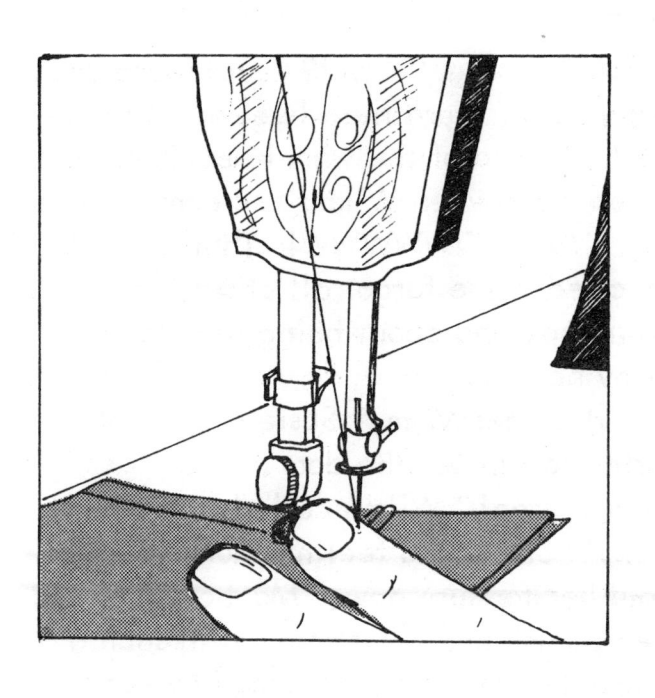

"Yes, but..."

"OOOOOOWWWWWWWWWWWWWW!"
screamed Wilma, so suddenly and so loudly that Susie jumped right out of her
chair. "OOOOOWWWWWWWWW!"

"What's wrong?" Susie asked.

"My finger! The needle went through
my finger!" Wilma wasn't sitting on her
chair now. She was jumping up and down
in pain.

"Can't you get it out?" Susie asked helplessly. "Turn the wheel backwards." She took hold of the wheel, but she hadn't turned a bit when Wilma's scream stopped her. "OOOOWWWWW! That hurts," she cried. She forgot all about being grown-up, and about being able to sew all by herself.

"I'll go get Mom," Susie said. She started to run out the door.

"No, stop!" Wilma called. "Come back." She had a feeling Mom would scold her for sure now. Maybe she would even punish her. But she was in such a bad spot. She needed Mom, and yet she was afraid to let Susie go get her.

"What are you going to do?" Susie asked. She sounded very frightened.

Wilma tried again to get the needle out of her finger, but it hurt too much. "All right, go call Mom," she finally said. Then she settled down to wait. She discovered that if she sat very still, her finger did not hurt quite so much. But even then it seemed like a long, long time until she heard Mom's footsteps on the porch.

Mom took one look at Wilma's finger, then she hurried to get the pliers. She quickly took off the clamp that held the needle in the sewing machine. Then Wilma's finger was free, but the needle was still in it.

With a quick little jerk, Mom pulled the needle out of Wilma's finger. It hurt, but it happened so fast that Wilma hardly had time to scream. But when she saw that the needle was finally out of her finger, she leaned against Mom and cried harder than ever.

Mom got a bottle of something that had a strong smell. She dipped Wilma's finger into it. "Shhh!" she said. "I know your finger hurts, but if you had waited until I helped you, this might not have happened."

"I — I didn't know this-s c-could happen," Wilma sobbed.

"I did," Mom said. "That is why I wanted you to wait until I was with you. You see, when Dad and I tell you to do something or not do something, we have a good reason for it. The reason is often that we do not want you to get hurt."

A few minutes later Mom had a neat little bandage on Wilma's finger, then she went back to the pea patch. Wilma sat on the couch, holding her sore finger in the other hand. She couldn't play all forenoon, so she just sat around. This gave her plenty of time to think.

"Mom didn't want me to get hurt," she thought. "That's why she didn't want me to sew by myself. The next time I'll wait. I don't want to get hurt again."

The Boy in the Wagon

Part 1: An Exciting Toy

"Oh, Mom, is this for us?" asked Elmer Miller. His eyes shone as he pulled a box from a paper bag. Mom had come home from town and the children were eager to see what she had bought.

"No, that is not for you," Mom answered. "Don't take it out of the box. It is for Andrew. He had a birthday last week."

Elmer was disappointed. He held the box and looked at the picture on it. It showed a train running through a tunnel. "You mean we may not even see it before we give it away?" he asked.

"We'll ask Dad. If he says it is all right, you three oldest boys may see how it works tonight when the younger children have gone to bed," Mom promised. "But please don't take it out of the box now."

Elmer handed the box back to Mom, but he didn't do it very willingly. "Why didn't you buy two of them?" he asked. "We'd like to have one, too."

Mom smiled. "You boys can go outside to play, so you don't need wind-up toys," she said. "I did buy a nice puzzle that we'll put together sometime."

Elmer cheered up a bit. "May I see it? How many pieces does it have?"

Mom handed him a box that had a picture of a horse and a colt on it. The two animals were in a green pasture, with mountains in the background. The mountains were covered with trees.

"Say, this is nice!" Elmer exclaimed. "It's going to be hard, too, with all those trees. It has five hundred pieces. This is the biggest puzzle we've had."

"I knew you'd like this picture," Mom said. "And now that you are older, you'll enjoy a puzzle with more pieces. Let's put it away until the corn is husked and the snow flies. Then we'll put it together. Right now I know one boy who has chores to do."

Elmer was still thinking about the puzzle and the toy train when he was doing his chores. His family enjoyed puzzles. As far back as he could remember, he liked helping to put them together. But right now, he would have chosen the train.

Elmer's thoughts went from the train to the boy who was going to get it. Andrew Raber was a crippled boy who lived about two miles away. He couldn't walk, and spent much of his time in a coaster wagon. The wagon had to have a padded rack around it. He could sit by himself, but he often lost his balance and fell.

When Andrew went to church, his father carried him into the house and put him into a rocking chair. Even there he had to be tied around the waist so that he would not fall out of it.

Once when Elmer had asked Mom about Andrew, she had explained that in many ways he would be like a little boy all his life. His brain had been damaged when

he was a baby. Therefore it did not grow like other children's brains do. Mom told him that Andrew would be one of God's special children all his life, and that Elmer was never, never to laugh at him or make fun of him in any way.

That evening Dad told the boys they could take the train out of the box and see how it worked. "If it breaks the first time it is used, we'd better not give it," he said.

The boys were eager and excited. They took the train and the track out of the box. They put the track together and set it up. They hooked the engine and the four cars together. Finally everything was ready. Elmer put the key into the hole in front of the engine and wound it up. Nothing happened.

"Here, pull this lever," John said.

The train jumped to life and rattled over the tracks. The boys watched excitedly. "Say, this is neat. Andrew will really like this," John said. "He likes anything that moves and makes a noise."

The boys each had a turn winding up the train. Then they had to take the set apart and put it back into the box. "We'll go over to the Rabers one of these even-ings. Then you can give the train to Andrew and set it up for him," Dad said.

"Oh, goody," Elmer said, pleased that he would have at least one more chance to play with the train. In his way of thinking, this was the most exciting toy he had ever seen. "I wish we could keep it," he thought. "We could have so much fun playing with it."

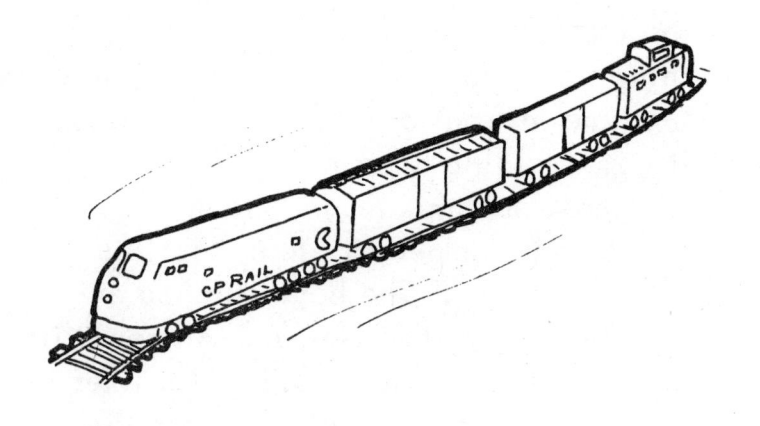

Part 2: Better Than Toys

Elmer still wanted to keep the train when they went to visit the Raber family, but he did not say anything about it to anyone. Even though he had wanted to carry the box with the train in it, he felt bashful about it when they got there. He tried to push the box into John's hands, but John didn't want it either. Elmer went over and tried to give it to Mom.

"Don't give it to me," Mom said. "Give it to Andrew."

Elmer put the box, which was still in the paper bag, into the wagon with Andrew. Andrew laughed out loud, but he did not try to open the box.

"You'll have to help him open it," Andrew's mother said.

Elmer felt even more bashful now. Everyone was watching him. But he took the box out of the bag. When he placed it in Andrew's hands, Andrew laughed out loud.

"Say 'Thank you,'" his mother said.

Andrew twisted his mouth for a while, and then a sound came out. It sure didn't sound like "Thank you" to Elmer.

"You're welcome!" Mom said, patting Andrew on the shoulder. "You had a birthday last week, didn't you?"

Andrew laughed again and tried to say something. He pointed to the table that stood in the corner of the kitchen.

"He wants you to see his new toys," Andrew's dad said. "Birthday time is a happy time for Andrew."

"I'll have to put most of those toys away and give them to him one by one," Mom Raber said. She was putting the last of the supper dishes away. "He has more than he can play with at one time."

The men went into the living room to visit. Mom Raber talked to the boys. "Would you like to put the train together for Andrew and show him how it works?" she asked. "He really enjoys having someone make his things go for him."

Once more the track was put together. The engine and the cars were hooked together and set on the tracks. Andrew, who sat on the floor now with pillows all around him, seemed to be having a very good time.

When everything was ready, Elmer was going to pull the lever to start the train. But John had a different idea. "Let Andrew start it," he said.

"Here, Andrew, pull this lever," Elmer said, pointing to it. Andrew reached out his hand, but he couldn't guide it to the right place. It seemed the harder he tried, the more his hand waved and jerked back and forth. Once he almost knocked down the track.

Andrew's brother, Daniel, knew just what to do. He took Andrew's hand and guided it to the right place. When the train started to go, Andrew jerked back in surprise. He lost his balance and fell over.

When the train stopped, Daniel helped Andrew sit up. He seemed eager to start the train again. This time he knew where the lever was, but he still needed someone to guide his hand to it. The minute the train started, Andrew's body jerked and he fell over again.

After a little while Elmer left the boys and the train and went over to see what else Andrew had. He could hardly believe his eyes when he saw all the different wind-up toys on the table. There was a fat bear pushing a wheelbarrow, a cat with a battery that lit up her eyes and made her walk at the same time, another train that ran on batteries and threw sparks as it rattled over the track, a Greyhound bus, and a turtle with a long neck that moved up and down as it walked slowly across the floor.

"People know Andrew likes things that move and make a noise," Daniel explained. "That's why he gets so many wind-up toys."

Soon the boys had all the toys on the
floor. They tried to keep them all moving at the same time. Some of them
went around in circles, while others
moved in a straight line.

It was hard to tell who enjoyed it
most — the boys who were playing with
the toys, or Andrew, who was watching.
He lay on the floor and laughed and
laughed. The boys did not help him sit
up any more. He was too excited to even
try to sit.

Elmer was having the best time he
could ever remember. All too soon the
evening was over and it was time to go
home. Elmer played as long as he could.
Then he quickly put on his wraps and
played some more.

117

"Maybe you'd like to stay here," Dad Raber said with a twinkle in his eye. "I am sure Andrew would enjoy having another brother."

Without a word Elmer put the Greyhound bus back on the table and followed the rest of the family out to the buggy. As they started home, he was thinking how lucky Daniel Raber was, having all those toys to play with every evening. Before long he put his thoughts into words. "I wish we had a boy like Andrew."

Mom was surprised. "Why do you wish that?" she asked.

"W-well, we — we could pull him around in his wagon and play with him," Elmer said, not giving the real reason at all.

"Which of your brothers would you want it to be?" Dad asked.

Elmer did some fast thinking. Not John, that was sure. Dad needed John to drive the horses and help with the field work. Nor could it be Amos, who was just younger than Elmer. Amos and Elmer

did a lot of things together, like climbing trees and running races and going fishing. They couldn't do any of these things if Amos were crippled.

That left only Jacob, the baby. Elmer thought of the good times they had had, teaching him to walk. He remembered how they had cheered when he was able to do it. Jacob with his round, healthy face and yellow curls? No, no! He did not want Jacob to be the boy in the wagon.

"Maybe you would want to be that boy yourself," Dad said. "Then all those toys would be yours. If they wore out, you would not need to worry about it. You would be sure to get some more on your next birthday."

Elmer shook his head back and forth, forgetting that Dad couldn't see him in the dark. Finally he said, "I — I meant, well, just some other boy."

"You're forgetting that any other boy in our family would be your brother, too," Dad reminded. Then giving Elmer a little more time to think about it, he said, "Don't you think Daniel Raber would gladly trade all those toys for a brother who had a healthy mind and body? I'm sure you would not have wished for a brother like Andrew, had you stopped to think about it."

Elmer thought about Andrew again. He had to sit on the wagon much of the time. He could not walk. He could not talk plainly. He couldn't do as much as reach out his hand and make it do what he wanted it to do. Now that Elmer thought about it, he couldn't think of a single thing Andrew could do as well as he could.

"Dad is right," Elmer thought. "I did not think. Healthy brothers and sisters are worth more than all the toys in the world."

Unit Three:

Learning

about Animals

The Animal of Surprises

Part 1: The Biggest Animal

It was Monday morning. Johnny Mast was walking to school with two of his friends. He was telling them about the sale he had been to on Saturday. "It was at my uncle's place," he said. "He is getting too old to run the farm, so he sold all his things. I thought it was fun, listening to the auctioneer."

"I know what an auctioneer sounds like," Wayne Troyer said. "Forty, forty, forty. Give me forty. And a half, half, half. Going, going, going — sold!"

The boys laughed. "You'll have to practice a while before you can be a real auctioneer," Johnny said. He wasn't through telling the boys about the sale. "The part I liked best was when they sold the horses. Uncle Dan had one horse that was really big. And was he nice! His coat was black and smooth and shiny. When they brought him out to sell, the auctioneer said, "Look what we have here — an elephant!"

"Oh, the horse wasn't that big," Wayne said. "Or maybe the auctioneer didn't know how big an elephant really is. That's the biggest animal in the world, and it is much, much bigger than a horse."

The boys had reached the schoolhouse, but they kept right on talking. "The elephant isn't the biggest animal in the world. The whale is," Johnny said.

"It is not," Wayne said. "And besides, a whale isn't an animal. Not really. It's a fish. Who ever heard of a fish being bigger than an elephant?"

"A fish is an animal," Johnny said. He felt a little hurt by the way Wayne talked. "And I'm almost sure I read somewhere that a whale is bigger than any other animal."

"Good morning, boys!" Teacher Mary said cheerfully.

"Good morning, Teacher," the boys returned.

"What are you saying about whales and elephants this morning?" the teacher asked.

The boys looked at each other and grinned. Then Wayne said, "Johnny said he saw a horse on Saturday that was as big as an elephant."

"I didn't say that," Johnny said quickly. "I said the auctioneer said he was as big as an elephant."

Teacher Mary smiled. "That was his way of saying the horse is very big, which it probably was."

"Oh, he was huge," Johnny said eagerly. "His legs were this thick." He made
a circle with his arms.

"An elephant's legs are much thicker
than that," Wayne said. "There's a picture in the encyclopedia of a man and an
elephant. The man is much smaller than
the elephant's leg."

"Elephants are huge," Teacher Mary agreed. "I wouldn't care to have one step on my toe." She paused, then said, "I thought I heard something about whales, too. They didn't sell anything as big as a whale, did they?"

"No. Johnny was just claiming that a whale is bigger than an elephant," Wayne said. He laughed. "And he said a whale is an animal."

"And you think he's wrong about that?" Teacher Mary said.

"Of course he's wrong," Wayne said. "A whale is a fish, because it lives in the water. Anyone knows that animals live on land and fish live in the water."

Teacher Mary started to say something, but then she didn't say it after all. "Would you like to learn more about elephants and whales?" she asked. "I think you would find it interesting."

Wayne was eager to learn more about these animals, but Johnny wasn't. He felt ashamed that he had been wrong, and he was sure Wayne would laugh at him some more about it.

"Come on, let's go out and play," he said, eager to talk about something else.

The boys went outside. By this time some more of the pupils had come, and were on the playground. It was not very cold, so it was a good morning to play "Prisoner's Base." Johnny joined the game. Soon he had forgotten about elephants and whales and big horses.

That day when the children came in from noon, Teacher Mary did not have her storybook in her hand like she usually did. She had an encyclopedia open in front of her. "We are going to do something different for a change," she began. "This morning a few of the boys were talking about the size of different animals. I thought it might be interesting to learn a bit more about them."

Johnny felt his face get red. Wayne turned around in his seat and looked at Johnny. He was grinning.

Johnny was glad Teacher Mary didn't say who the boys were. She just went on with what she had to say. "This lesson will be mostly for the lower graders, but

the older pupils may listen, too. You
will find it interesting, and we'll need
your help in answering questions." Turning to the younger children, she asked,
"How many of you have seen an elephant
— a real, live elephant?"

Hands went up. Some of the children
had been to the zoo and had seen an elephant. But others had not. "I have seen
a picture of one," a first-grade boy said.

Wayne raised his hand. "Seeing a picture isn't like seeing a real elephant," he
said, sounding important. "A picture
doesn't show how big it really is."

"No, it doesn't, but it gives us an idea what an elephant looks like," she said, holding up the encyclopedia so the children could see the picture. "This is what an elephant looks like. Do you see his trunk, his big flappy ears, and his big feet and legs? Now, let's try to get an idea of his size. If we brought an elephant into this classroom, do you think he would reach the ceiling?"

Wayne nearly jumped out of his seat. "You couldn't bring an elephant in here because the door isn't wide enough," he said.

"Yes, that's right," the teacher said. "But let's pretend that the door is wide enough. How close to the ceiling do you think the elephant's head would be?"

A third-grade girl raised her hand. "I think he could reach the ceiling with his trunk," she said.

"Do the rest of you agree?" the teacher asked.

Most of the children did. They thought the elephant could surely reach the ceiling with his trunk.

"Does anyone think his head might reach the ceiling?" the teacher asked. She smiled at the upper graders who raised their hands. "Let's ask the lower graders."

Some of the children nodded, but most of them shrugged their shoulders. Even Wayne was unsure of himself. They all sat there, looking at the ceiling.

"I have news for you," Teacher Mary said. "This classroom is eight feet high. A full-grown elephant is from ten to twelve feet tall. That means it could not stand up in this classroom. The ceiling is too low."

There were gasps of surprise among the children. They looked at each other and then at the ceiling again. Even Wayne could hardly believe it. "I knew elephants were big, but I didn't know they were that big," he said. "The ones we saw at the zoo didn't look that big."

"You could be right, Wayne," Teacher Mary said. "Elephants that are raised in the zoo do not get as big as those that grow up in the jungles. Also, you may have seen an Asian elephant. They are not as big as those that come from Africa, which is the one I was describing. But I think maybe the elephants you saw were bigger than you realized. Can anyone explain why?"

An eighth-grade boy raised his hand. "They were probably outside when he saw them."

"That's right," Teacher Mary said. "When something is outside in an open space, we often do not realize how big it really is. But we know one thing. Anyone having a pet elephant may not bring it to school. Our classroom isn't high enough."

The children giggled.

Teacher Mary glanced at the clock. "Our story time is up. We have only started talking about the elephant. Tomorrow we'll learn some more about this huge animal. But right now it is time to get to our other work."

Part 2: More About the Elephant

The boys and girls at Teacher Mary's school looked forward to story time the next day. They were eager to learn more about these giant animals.

"Yesterday we talked about how big an elephant is," Teacher Mary said. "Today we want to think about its weight. How much does an elephant weigh?"

"About six or seven tons," one of the boys said.

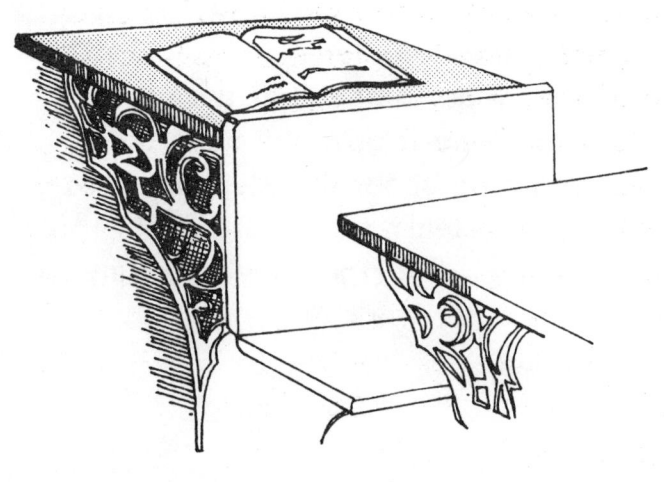

"That's right, but how much is that?" the teacher asked.

"Twelve or fourteen thousand pounds," said one of the girls.

"Yes," Teacher Mary said. But she still wasn't satisfied. "We need something to compare it with."

A boy raised his hand. "The truck that delivers feed to our place holds seven tons."

"That helps," Teacher Mary said. "An elephant weighs as much as a truck load of feed." Then an idea came to her mind. "Let's suppose we had a pet elephant and it died. It's out here on the playground, dead. A truck has come to haul it away. How many men is it going to take to lift the elephant on the truck?"

Some of the children were ready to guess.

"Ten," they said.

"More than that," another one said.

"No, not more than ten."

An eighth grader raised his hand. "We have to know how much each one is going to lift," he said.

"Let's say about one hundred pounds,"
Teacher Mary said. "We don't want anyone to hurt his back."

The boy put down his pencil. "That's
easy," he said. "If the elephant weighs
fourteen thousand pounds, it would take
one hundred forty men to lift him."

"No, you made a mistake," one of the
big girls said. But after she had figured
it out with her pencil, she had to admit
that the boy was right after all. The
children gasped with surprise. And this
was just the beginning of many amazing
things they learned about the elephant.

They learned that a baby elephant weighs about two hundred pounds when it is born. It stays with its mother and drinks milk for two or three years. It does not find this milk between its mother's hind legs like a colt or a calf does, but between its mother's front legs.

Elephants have a trunk, which is a wonder in itself. There are no bones in the trunk — just flesh and muscles. It is six feet long and weighs three hundred pounds. The elephant uses its trunk to eat and to drink. The trunk is also the elephant's nose, and few animals have a better one. An elephant has a very keen sense of smell.

The tip of the elephant's trunk is used much like a person uses his hand. It can pick up small things like peanuts and other tiny bits of food. It also tells the elephant how something feels — whether it is rough or smooth, hot or cold, hard or soft.

The elephant has other uses for its trunk. In warm weather elephants often stand in water up to their knees. They keep cool by filling the trunk with water and spraying it over their body. They also use their trunk to fight and to dig for food. Trained elephants work with their trunk. They can lift and carry loads weighing up to a ton with their trunk.

An elephant also has tusks, which are really great big teeth. They stick out of the front of the mouth, and make an elephant look dangerous. The tusks may be as much as six or eight feet long. Its grinding teeth, the ones inside its mouth, are at least a foot long, and weigh eight or nine pounds each.

The boys and girls enjoyed learning about the elephant. They named it "The Animal of Surprises," because so many things about it were different from what they expected them to be.

One thing they were amazed about was its feet. "An elephant never gets stuck in the mud," Teacher Mary told them. She reminded them that elephants live in wet, rainy jungles. There the ground is often muddy. Weighing as much as they do, they sink into the mud when they walk. But no matter how muddy it is, they never get stuck. Their feet spread out when weight is put on them. When the elephant lifts his foot, it becomes smaller. That makes it possible for him to lift his foot out of the mud.

The children also learned that some people who live across the sea own elephants, just as farmers own horses. But most of these animals are not born on the farm like colts are. They are captured in the jungles and brought home.

Elephants are captured in different ways. If many of them are needed, several hundred men get together. They make a big circle around a herd of elephants. Then when everyone is ready, the men all start making loud noises. The elephants become frightened, and start to run. By running after them and making noises, the men chase them into very strong pens. There they are kept and fed until they are used to people. Then they are trained, much like horses are trained in our land.

If only one or two elephants are needed, there are other ways of capturing them. One is to dig a big hole and cover it with branches and leaves. When an elephant comes along, he falls into the hole. The men feed him and tame him. When they think it is safe to let him out, they throw logs into the hole. As the hole fills up, the elephant comes up, higher and higher. At last he is able to climb out of the hole.

Still another way of capturing an elephant is to let a tame one go into the jungle and make friends with a wild one.

While the wild elephant has his attention
on the tame one, a man slips up and puts
a heavy chain around his hind leg. The
other end of the chain has been fastened
to a big tree. When the elephant tries
to walk away, he discovers that he is tied
to the tree.

He roars in anger, but he can not get
away. The people who have captured
him know enough to stay away. They also know that if he is given enough time,
the elephant will become tame. Soon he
is tired and hungry. The men come to
feed him. They do not come too close,
for an angry elephant can kill a man with
one swing of his powerful trunk. But if
he is treated kindly and gently, he soon
becomes tame. It is not hard to train an
elephant, for he has a keen memory.
Once he has learned something, he will
not forget it.

Teacher Mary was just ready to close
her book and tell the children to get
back to work when one of the girls raised
her hand. "What do elephants eat?" she
asked.

"Who can answer Ella's question?" the teacher asked.

Wayne raised his hand. "Peanuts," he answered.

"Yes, they eat peanuts. They love them, but just think how many peanuts it would take to fill his big stomach," the teacher said.

"The elephants we saw at the zoo were eating hay," another boy said.

"That is what elephants in our country eat," Teacher Mary said. "Wild ones eat grass, leaves, branches, and bark. They love wild berries, too, and sugar cane and certain kinds of nuts. The encyclopedia says elephants are not very polite with their eating habits. They chew noisily, and their stomachs rumble as they eat. When they get thirsty, they suck water into their trunk. Then they open their mouth and squirt it in. It makes a loud noise as it bubbles down their throat."

The children laughed. The teacher closed her book. "How many of you have enjoyed learning about the elephant?" she asked.

Hands went up. Everyone thought the elephant, a giant among animals, was an interesting creature.

"Would you like to learn about another big animal?" the teacher asked. "One that is even bigger than an elephant?"

Johnny sat up straight. Had he heard right? Did the teacher really say bigger than an elephant. Maybe he was right after all.

The children all nodded their heads. Some of them raised their hands. "We know what it is," they whispered.

"Shhh!" the teacher said. "Let's forget about big animals now and get to work. Let's not think about them until story time tomorrow."

A Giant and Its Baby

Even though Teacher Mary had told her
pupils to forget about animals until the
next day, they kept talking about them.
It was not long until everyone knew that
the big animal their teacher had in mind
was the whale. But some of them, like
Wayne, insisted that a whale was a fish
and not an animal.

"A fish may be a little like an animal,
but it isn't really one," Wayne said that
evening on the way home from school.
"A bird isn't an animal either, and nei-
ther is an insect. My big brother once
laughed at me when I said a bug is an
animal. That is when I found out about
the different kinds of creatures — animals,
insects, fish, reptiles, and things like
that.

"What's a reptile?" Johnny wanted to
know. He was the oldest child in his
family, and didn't have a big brother to
teach him these things.

"Snakes and lizards are reptiles,"
Wayne said, eager to show Johnny how
much he knew. "Turtles are, too, and
alligators. Anything that likes to be in
the water and swim is a reptile."

"Then a fish is a reptile, too," Johnny
said.

"Oh, no. I forgot to tell you. A reptile has to come out of the water to
breathe. Fish breathe in the water.
They die if they are taken out of the
water. That's what makes a whale a fish
and not an animal. Teacher Mary can
call it whatever she wants to. I'm still
going to call a whale a fish."

Even though Wayne knew a lot about animals and fish and reptiles, he did not know as much as he thought he did. He found that out the next day. When story time came, Teacher Mary was ready. She had the "W" encyclopedia in her hand. She had made notes of the things she wanted the children to learn.

"The first thing we are going to get straight is something I heard you disagree about. That is whether a whale is a fish or an animal. All living things, other than plants, are classed as animals. That makes fish and worms and birds and insects all animals. But I know what you mean when you say whales are not animals. Birds are one type of animal. Fish are another type, and so are reptiles and insects. We have a special name for animals such as horses and pigs and cows and the many others that we usually call animals. I'll write it on the board."

In large letters, Teacher Mary wrote mammals on the board. She had even the first graders repeat the word so they would not forget it. Then she went on with her lesson. "Let's compare mammals with fish. In what ways are they different?"

Wayne's hand shot up. "Fish live in water," he said.

"Right," the teacher said. "What else?"

"Mammals breathe through their lungs and fish do not," another pupil said.

"Who knows how fish get their air?" the teacher asked.

"Through their gills," said an eighth grader.

"Good," Teacher Mary said. "In what other ways are mammals and fish different from each other?

"Fish lay eggs," said one of the girls.

"Let's say most fish lay eggs," Teacher Mary said. "I think there are some kinds of fish that give birth to baby fish." She paused, then said, "There is something about the way mother mammals feed their babies that make them different from any other animals."

Five or six children raised their hands. "Mammals feed their babies with milk," one of them said.

"That's right," Teacher Mary said.
She smiled at the eager children. "Now,
let's get back to whales. I'd like to help
you decide whether the whale is a fish or
a mammal. I'll read this paragraph to
you."

She opened the book and read, "'The
whale is the biggest animal in the world.
The largest kind of whale, the giant blue
whale, may grow ninety-five feet long
and weigh one hundred and fifty tons. A
newborn baby whale may weigh three tons
and measure more than twenty feet long.'"

Johnny smiled to himself. So he was
right after all. The encyclopedia said
the whale was the biggest animal in the
world, so it had to be bigger than an
elephant.

Wayne, however, did not give up easily. "Why does that book say a whale is
an animal, when it really is a fish?"

"What makes you think it is a fish?"
Teacher Mary asked.

"It lives in the water, and it — it looks
like a fish," Wayne answered.

"I'll read the next paragraph, then you can decide for yourself," Teacher Mary said. "Listen carefully. 'Whales live in oceans and look like fish, but they are not fish. They are mammals, just like dogs and cats and horses and cows. Mother whales give birth to baby whales, and they feed them with milk. They breathe through lungs and must hold their breath when they are in the water. They drown if they are trapped under water and can not come to the surface for air.'"

The teacher looked up and smiled. "Yesterday we decided the elephant was the animal of surprises. I think we'll soon say the same thing about the whale."

"We tried to tell Wayne and some of the others that whales are not fish, but they wouldn't believe it," a fifth-grade boy said. "I once read a book about whales. I learned then that whales are mammals."

"Sometimes things are different from what we think they are," Teacher Mary said. "It's always best not to be too sure. We could be wrong."

Johnny smiled to himself, but he decided not to tease Wayne. No doubt he felt bad enough about it already.

The teacher turned back to her book. "Here is something we forgot when we compared fish and mammals," she said. "Fish are cold-blooded animals, and mammals are warm-blooded. People are warm-blooded. When we go out on a very cold day, the inside of our body does not cool off. The temperature stays the same. But the body temperature of a fish changes. If the water is cold, its temperature goes down. If the water is warm, a fish's body becomes warm, too. Whales are not like that. Whales are warm-blooded animals. They have a thick layer of fat, called blubber, under their skin to keep their bodies warm, even when they swim in cold water."

A second-grade girl raised her hand. "How many men would it take to lift a whale?" she asked.

"That's an interesting question," Teacher Mary said. "We'll get to it as soon as we've made ourselves a picture of how big a blue whale is. The book says ninety-five feet. How long is that?"

William Miller raised his hand. "That chicken house over there is a hundred feet long," he said, pointing across the field to a long, low building on their farm.

"That gives us a good idea," Teacher Mary said. "Try to picture a whale almost as long as that chicken house. If I remember right, this schoolhouse is thirty feet long. A whale is about three times as long as this schoolhouse. Or if we want to compare it with an elephant, about eight or nine elephants could stand along a whale's back."

One of the boys gave out a whistle of surprise.

"Let's talk about weight now," Teacher Mary went on. "Edna wants to know how many men it would take to lift a whale. Who can tell her?"

The upper graders did some fast thinking. "Three thousand," one of them said.
"No, it can't be that many. You made
a mistake," another boy said.
The boy had not made a mistake.
Teacher Mary said a blue whale weighed
one hundred fifty tons, which was three
hundred thousand pounds. If each man
lifted one hundred pounds, it would take
three thousand men to lift a whale. "This
shows how very big whales really are,"
Teacher Mary said. "Just think how
much food such a huge animal would eat."
"What do whales eat?" Johnny asked.
Teacher Mary asked the children if
they knew. Some thought they ate small
fish. Others thought they ate seaweeds
and moss. Still others said they ate insects that floated on the surface of the
water. The teacher said they were all
right. There were many different kinds
of whales, and each one had its own
food. She explained that there were so
many plants in the ocean, both on the
surface and on the bottom, that there was
plenty of food for the many creatures that
lived in the water.

"If whales have lungs and breathe air, how can they live in the water?" someone wanted to know.

Teacher Mary asked an eighth-grade boy to explain. "They don't breathe all the time like we do," he said. "They can take in enough air to last anywhere from ten to forty-five minutes. Then they have to come to the surface, empty their lungs, and take in some fresh air."

"That's right," Teacher Mary said. She glanced at the clock. Story time was over. In fact, it had gone longer than the usual fifteen minutes. "I think we are learning more from the encyclopedias than we have from any other book."

The children agreed. They had learned a lot, but they still weren't satisfied. "Let's learn some more about unusual animals," they said.

The Camel Bird

The next day at story time, Teacher Mary had the "O" encyclopedia in her hand. The children tried to guess what animal they would learn about that day. They soon discovered they couldn't think of many animals that start with "O."

When the children were all in their seats and ready, the teacher began. "Yesterday we learned about the world's biggest mammal. Today we'll study another giant — the world's biggest living bird. Who can tell the class what it is?"

"The ostrich," answered a seventh-grade girl.

"I don't think we'll have as many surprises today as we did on the other days," another girl said. "Birds aren't as unusual as some animals are. They aren't as interesting either, I don't think."

"How many of you agree with Ella?" Teacher Mary asked.

A few of the children did. Others weren't sure.

Teacher Mary smiled. "If you keep your ears open, you will find out that the bird we are about to study is every bit as interesting and unusual as any animal. I think I will begin by reading a few paragraphs to you."

She opened the book and started to read. "'In many ways the ostrich is not like other birds. For one thing, it can't fly. It has wings, but they are short and stubby. They are not large enough to lift the weight of this huge bird from the ground.

'Years ago people called the ostrich the camel bird, because in many ways it is more like a camel than a bird. It even looks like a camel. It has that same humping walk. It sways back and forth when it runs, very much like a camel does.

'The ostrich is like the camel in another way. It can go without water for a long time. This is important to the ostrich, because it lives mostly in dry places. Many ostriches live on the desert.'" Teacher Mary paused. "Let's explain to the younger children what a desert is."

Johnny raised his hand. This was one question he could answer. "It is very dry there, because it does not rain much."

"Right," Teacher Mary said. "And because it is so dry, not much grows there. Some deserts are bare and sandy, but others have a poor grade of grass and even a few small trees." She showed the children a picture of some ostriches. "This bird stands seven or eight feet tall and weighs up to three hundred pounds."

Edna raised her hand. "An ostrich would reach the ceiling in here," she said.

"That's right," Teacher Mary said. "Imagine a bird so large that his head would reach the ceiling in this class-room."

"It would only take three men to lift a dead ostrich," another pupil said.

"Yes, compared with an elephant or a whale, an ostrich is not very big. But when we compare it with other birds we know, it is quite big," Teacher Mary said. "Take, for example, an ostrich's egg. It says here an egg from this bird weighs three pounds, which is also what baby ostriches weigh when they hatch. They are almost as big as a full-grown barnyard hen."

The children gasped. A baby bird as big as a hen! Teacher Mary went right on. "'Size is not the only thing that is unusual about this bird. Even though it can not fly, it has ways of its own to protect itself. It can run fifty miles an hour, which is faster than a horse or even a jack rabbit. There is only one other animal that can run faster, and that is a certain kind of wild cat.

'Running is not the only way an ostrich can protect itself. It has very powerful legs. With these legs, an ostrich can kick hard enough to break a man's leg or even kill him.'"

Once more the children were surprised. "Imagine, a bird that can kick hard enough to kill a man!" one of them said.

There were more surprises in store for the children. The teacher read on. "'Ostriches are handsome creatures. Some of them are black and shiny, with pure white wing and tail plumes. However, their voices do not match these plumes in beauty. They roar deeply, like a lion or an ox. At other times they hiss loudly.

'Ostriches can see very well. Their necks are about three feet long, and their small heads are perched on top of these long necks. With their two big eyes, they can see for miles across the level desert.'"

Eli, an eighth-grade boy, raised his hand. "That is why it is so hard to study wild ostriches," he said. "I once read a book that said people didn't know much about them for a long time. The ostriches always ran away when people came to

study them. Then a man and his wife played a trick on them. They made a place to hide on the desert. They covered their hiding place to make it look like a big ant hill. They sat inside and waited. The ostriches walked right up to the make-believe ant hill. The people sat inside and watched them. That is how they learned more about them."

"It's a wonder the ostriches didn't smell the people and run away," Wayne said.

"Their sense of smell must not be as keen as that of the elephant," Teacher Mary said. "Remember what we read about the elephant's nose?"

"It is better than any other animal's nose," one of the children answered.

"Yes, and its eyesight is poor," Teacher Mary said. "But here we have an animal that can see very well, but does not have a keen sense of smell. Isn't it wonderful how each animal is different, but it has what it needs to protect itself and to find food?"

"What do ostriches eat?" one of the younger children asked.

"We're just getting to that," Teacher Mary said. She turned the page of the encyclopedia and read on, "'Ostriches eat grass, leaves, berries, seeds, and fruit. They also eat insects and even birds. Ostriches in zoos are mostly fed on grain and certain kinds of hay. They will swallow stones, bits of broken glass, bones, and many other hard things.'"

"They eat many different kinds of food," a fifth grader said.

"Yes, they do," Teacher Mary agreed. "Here is something else I found interesting. Ostrich hens do not all have their own nests. As many as four or five of them lay their eggs in one nest. Then one of them sits on the eggs in the daytime — not to keep them warm as you might expect, but to keep them cool! Remember that they live on the desert where it gets very warm when the sun shines. By sitting on the nest and spreading out its wings, an ostrich hen protects the eggs from the heat of the sun.

"Then when the sun is no longer so hot, it is Daddy Ostrich's turn to sit on the eggs. He keeps them warm during the night, until the sun rises in the morning. Usually the ostrich hen is on the nest about eight hours of the day, and the father ostrich for the remaining sixteen hours.

"It takes about six weeks for ostrich eggs to hatch. Baby ostriches do not take much care. They can run almost as soon as they are hatched, and they find their own food." Teacher Mary stopped and looked at the clock. "Our time is almost up," she said. "But there is one more thing we want to learn about this un-usual bird. Who would like to guess how old an ostrich might become?"

"Ten years," said Wayne.

"Eight," guessed someone else.

"Twenty-five," said an upper-grader.

Some of the children shook their heads and laughed. "Who ever heard of a bird getting that old?" they asked.

161

"This is still another way in which an ostrich is a bird of surprises," Teacher Mary said. "They grow very fast. Six months after they have hatched, they are as big as their parents. And they are grown-up ostriches for a long time, because some of them live to be eighty years old."

"Are you sure it's not eight, or eighteen?" a seventh-grade girl asked.

"I looked twice myself, but it is eighty," Teacher Mary said.

"That's older than my grandfather," Wayne said.

Rebecca, an eighth-grade girl, asked, "Are ostriches ever killed for food? I was just thinking about how much meat there would be on a bird weighing three hundred pounds."

"You mean on a neck three feet long," Teacher Mary chuckled. "I wondered about the same thing, but it says here ostrich meat is not good to eat. It is tough and has a bad flavor. But there was a time when people had ostrich farms for another reason. Their plumes were in style, so farmers raised ostriches and sold the plumes. Ladies and men wore ostrich plumes in their hats, or pinned them to their coats and dresses. But they have gone out of style now, and ostrich farms are no longer common."

Teacher Mary closed her book with a bang. "Time to get to work," she said. But then she paused. "I've been thinking about the animals and birds we have studied. We've picked some very unusual ones. Let's not get the idea that animals in faraway lands and those living in zoos

are the only ones that are interesting.
We have some very interesting ones right
here at home."

"What are they?" the children asked
eagerly. They enjoyed talking about animals better than they enjoyed doing their
other lessons.

"There are many, and I'm going to ask
the older pupils to write reports on some
of them. We'll read these reports during
story time. Would you like that?"

"Yes, yes," said the younger children.
The older ones were not quite so sure.
They were the ones who would have to
write the reports. But once the teacher
got them started, they enjoyed writing the
reports as much as the younger children
enjoyed listening to them.

The Purple Martin

Purple martins are many people's favorite birds. They have a clear, ringing song that is music to bird lovers. They are a pretty bird, too. The male has a purplish blue back that flashes in the sunlight. The female is not blue or purple. It is black and has a gray underside. Young martins all look like females. It is not until the second summer that the males get their pretty blue feathers.

Martins are graceful birds. They swoop and dive through the air so easily that it looks as if they were riding on the wind. Often they glide along without flapping their wings.

There is another reason why many people like purple martins. They are helpful birds, because they eat many insects. A single martin may eat as many as four hundred flies or two thousand mosquitoes in one day. This means if you have one martin family living in your yard — a male and a female and five little ones — they are eating close to three thousand flies a day. Just think how many they eat in a whole summer!

Martins do not eat just flies and mosquitoes, but all kinds of flying insects. A man who had a large peach orchard lost most of his crop one year. A harmful insect had damaged the fruit. The next year he put up a row of martin houses near his orchard. Some martins came and lived in them. That year he still had some damage from this insect, but not as much as the year before.

The next year more martins came to live in this man's houses. Still more came the next year. He found out that the more martins he had, the less damage the insects did to his peaches. No wonder he liked these birds. They saved him thousands of dollars worth of fruit each year.

Martins do not eat any grain, nor do they steal fruit from the farmers' orchards or berry patches. There are few birds that do so much good and so little harm as the martins do.

The people who live in the north look forward to seeing martins each spring. They usually see the first ones around the first of April. The males come first, and are soon joined by their mates. Once martins have stayed in a house overnight, there is a good chance that they will live there. They fly around, singing happily and catching insects for a few weeks. Then they start building their nest. Both the male and the female help with the nest. They use twigs, sticks, straw, and mud.

It is interesting to watch martins build their nests. Sometimes the sticks they carry to the house are too long to go through the doorway. One martin was seen to try three different doorways with a stick that was much too long to go through. Finally he dropped it and went to find a shorter one. Somehow, it didn't come to his mind to turn the stick sideways to take it in.

After the nest is finished, the female
martin lays from two to seven white eggs.
Often there are five. She sits on the nest
to keep the eggs warm. Even though the
male guards the nest when his mate goes
away, he does not sit on the eggs. But as
soon as the birds are hatched, he helps to
feed the new family.

A baby martin is not at all pretty. It
does not have any feathers. Its skin is
bare and wrinkled, as if it were much too
big for its tiny body. The baby birds are
weak. They lie in the nest with their
necks stretched out. Their heads are resting on the floor on the side of the nest.
When a parent bird comes with food, they
are barely strong enough to open their
bills.

It is very interesting to watch a pair of martins feed a family of babies. What busy parents they are! Sometimes they come to the nest with food three times a minute. Even though the babies' stomachs are small, it takes many, many insects to keep them fed. It seems there is never a time when the babies are not all hungry.

Within a few days, the babies become stronger. They sit up in the nest and are able to hold their heads. Within a week or ten days, the little heads can be seen in the doorway of the martins' home. When the parents come with food, the heads pop out of the hole. Each baby hopes it is his turn to get the food.

Baby martins stay in their nest three or four weeks. Sometimes they hop out onto the porch and sit there before they can fly. They add to the parents' music with chirps of their own.

Then one day they decide they can fly. Sometimes the parents have to decide for them. They push the young martin off its perch, forcing it to fly. The first flight is often only one circle over the martin

house. Then the young bird will return to
its perch, or even to the nest. But it will
not be long until it tries again. Within
a day, it is circling and diving and swoop-
ing as gracefully as its parents.

Like all other birds and animals, martins
have enemies. The most common one,
especially in some areas, is snakes.
Snakes climb the pole of the martin house.
They rob the nests, eating the eggs of the
young birds they find there. Cats sometimes do the same thing, as do certain
kinds of squirrels.

Parent birds let themselves be heard when there is danger near. They fly about, chattering and scolding loudly. Sometimes it is possible to save the eggs and baby birds by chasing off or killing whatever is after them. Martins seem to remember danger. Sometimes they move out of a house after it has been robbed by an enemy, and do not return to it for a long time.

Even the parent birds must be on the lookout for danger. They seldom sit on the ground, so it is not often that a cat will catch a full-grown martin. But certain kinds of owls will make a meal of a purple martin if they can.

Since martins live entirely on insects, they must go where they can find them. Insects do not fly in cold weather, so martins can not live when it gets cold. Early in the fall, usually around the first of August, the martins get restless. It is not that insects are scarce. They are as plentiful at that time of the year as they ever are. But something seems to tell the martins that it is time to move south.

The young birds are fully grown by this
time. They can fly well and are able to
find their own food. Big flocks of martins,
both young and old, gather together and
sit in long lines on fences and wires.
They chatter nervously, as if telling each
other that it is time to get started.

Then one day they are gone. The yard seems empty and silent without them, but bird lovers know it is good that they have gone. They could not survive the cold winter in the north.

The birds fly steadily, stopping now and then to rest a short while, but then they are on their way again. They fly over land and over water, mostly in a straight line. At night they usually find resting places in trees or on wires, and early the next morning they are on their way again.

Martins spend their winters in lands where it is warm the year round. When the right time comes, they start north again, arriving around the middle of April. The most amazing part of it is, many of them return to the same houses where they lived the year before.

How can these little birds fly thou-sands of miles and find their way back to the same spot they were the summer be-fore? How do martins, especially those which were hatched that summer, know that they must go south? Who tells them that a time is coming when they cannot find any insects to eat? How do they know they will die of hunger and from the cold if they do not fly to warmer lands?

The wise men of this world have been trying to find the answers to these questions, but many of them are still a mystery. We know that God made the birds and gave them a very special gift called instinct. This means they know certain things without having to learn them.

Many birds and animals do things by instinct, and going to warmer lands during the winter is one of them. It is instinct that tells them when to go and where. It is also instinct that guides them back to their homes in the north, and tells them it is time to build a nest and get ready to raise another family of little ones.

All the while the purple martins are doing this, they are cheering people with their songs. They are also eating hundreds and thousands of harmful insects. It is no wonder that the purple martin is many people's favorite bird.

Honeybees

Bees are insects that live in every part of the world. Only the lands near the North Pole and the South Pole, where it stays cold the year round, have no bees. There are ten thousand different kinds of bees, but only one kind that makes honey. They are called honeybees. They are the only insect in the world that produce food for man.

If you could catch a honeybee and take a good look at it, you would be in for a surprise. A bee has five eyes. Three of them are located on the top of the head. They are small and look like three dots. Then a bee also has two larger eyes, one on each side of the head.

Two feelers stick out of a bee's head. Even though you can not see them, these feelers are covered with tiny hair. These hair give the bee a sense of touch. They use them the same way you use your hands to examine something in the dark.

Perhaps the most unusual part of the bee is its mouth and tongue. The tongue is really a tube. The bee drinks through its tongue much like you drink milk through a straw. The tongue can be made longer or shorter, and it can move out of the mouth in every direction.

A bee has four wings. When it flies, the two wings on each side of the body hook together and work as one wing. The wings can move up and down, forwards and backwards. Because of this, a bee can fly backwards as well as forwards, and even sideways. It can also stay at one spot in the air and not move at all.

A bee has six legs, three on each side of the body. Many people believe that bees sting with one of these legs. They do not. The stinger is located at the very tip of the body. It has tiny barbs that make it stay in whatever the bee has

stung. This causes the bee to die a few
hours later. A bee can not live without
its stinger.

The stinger has poison in it that kills
an enemy if it is small enough. People
who get stung feel a burning pain. Soon
they see a red bump. This is caused by
the poison in the bee's stinger.

Some people are afraid of bees because they sting. But they do not sting unless they are frightened or hurt. Bees are man's friends. They make honey for us, which is something no other creature can do.

Bees help us in another way that is even more important than making honey. Nearly all the fruits and vegetables we eat grow from flowers. The trees and plants they grow on get flowers before they bear fruit. These flowers are called blossoms.

We have all seen trees that were covered with white or pink flowers in the spring. We have seen the little yellow flowers in the melon patch, and the white flowers on strawberry plants. These trees and plants were blooming, getting ready to bear fruit.

On these blossoms are tiny yellow grains called pollen. Unless this pollen is carried from one flower to the other, the fruit will not grow. Sometimes pollen drops from one flower to those under it. Sometimes the wind spreads the pollen from one flower to the other. But bees do more than anything else to spread the pollen.

Bees like pollen. They use it for food. But they do not come out into the field to eat it. The worker bees gather the pollen and store it in little bags on their legs. When they have all they can carry, they take it back to the hive. But they do not take it all back. As they crawl over the flowers, they drop some of the pollen. In this way, they spread pollen from one flower to the other.

Bees do not fly when the weather is cool and rainy. In some years the weather is cool and rainy when the fruit trees are blooming. Then there will not be as much fruit. The bees could not do their work at the right time.

Bees get something else besides pollen from flowers. They get nectar, too. Nectar is a sweet, sticky juice. Worker bees have a special stomach, called a honey sack, in which they carry the nectar to the hives. Bees use nectar to make honey.

A single bee living by itself could not survive. It needs the help of many other bees in order to stay alive. One bee can

not do much. It can not even do enough
to make it possible to stay alive! But by
working together with many other bees,
they can do amazing things.

Bees live in homes called hives. These
hives may be in hollow trees, in fallen
logs, or in special boxes made by man.
In many ways, bees work like people.
They build homes. They plan ahead.
They take care of the young bees while
they are helpless, and put them to work
as soon as they are old enough to help.

Each bee has a special job. They work
together in a very interesting and amazing way. Each hive has a queen bee. It
is her job to lay the eggs. But first the
worker bees must make a suitable place
for the queen to lay her eggs. They build
cells out of wax — thousands of them.

The queen bee is not like the barnyard hen, which lays only one egg a day. It lays as many as two thousand eggs a day. They are white, and about the size of the period at the end of this sentence.

As soon as an egg is laid, there is work for the worker bees. They feed the egg and seal it into the cell. There the egg grows and goes through different stages. Then one day, about three weeks after the queen has laid the egg, the young bee breaks the seal and comes out of the cell. It is not a baby bee, but a full-grown one. It is ready to help work.

The young bees are the housekeepers. They clean out the cells and get them ready for another egg. They help take care of the eggs as they are laid. Some of them are guards. They stay near the doorway of the hive and watch for ene-mies. They also watch for bees that do not belong to their hive, and chase them off.

If an enemy, such as an ant, a bug, or even a mouse comes into the hive, the bees attack it and sting it to death. After they have done this, they die, too. They have lost their stinger in the fight, and a bee can not live without its stinger. In this way, many bees die in protecting their home.

Other bees do the fanning. They sit near the doorway and fan their wings. This brings fresh air into the hive and forces the old air out. It also keeps the hive cool so the bees can do their work.

When a bee is from ten to fifteen days old, it goes out to find nectar and pollen. But where does it go? Must each bee search until it has found blossoms that make good honey? No. When a worker bee brings nectar back to the hive, it dances around on the floor. The other bees watch it, because it is telling in which direction from the hive, and how far away the flowers are.

When a bee leaves the hive and is on its way to the field, it often flies in a wavy line. Sometimes it even circles around a bit. But once it is loaded and on its way to the hive, it flies in a straight line. This is often called a bee-line. They do not need to pause or slow down. They zoom right into the hole of the hive.

If a beekeeper moves his hive, the bees have trouble finding it. If he moves it only a few inches, the bees will miss the hole and bump into the side of the box. But they soon learn to adjust to the new place, and make a beeline for it.

During the summer, when the bees work hard, they seldom live for more than six weeks. In the winter, when there is less work to be done, they live for several months. They stay in the hive and cling together in one big pile. The ones on the outside of the pile fan their wings. This time they are not cooling the hive, but warming the bees.

The bees on the outside may freeze, but those on the inside stay warm enough to survive. They usually live long enough the next spring to take care of the queen's first eggs, and until the young bees are able to take on the work of the hive.

How much work does a bee do in its lifetime? Not very much. Even though they work every day and kill themselves by working hard, it takes ten bees all their lives to produce one pound of honey. In order to do this, they make hundreds and hundreds of trips from the hive to the fields. A bee flies thousands of miles in its short lifetime.

It is the number of bees in a hive that makes it possible for them to produce enough food for themselves and for man. There are from sixty to eighty thousand bees in a good, strong hive. By working together they can produce all the honey they need, and then some.

A beekeeper knows that he may not take all the honey out of the hive in the fall. If he takes too much, the bees will starve during the winter. Instinct tells the bees that they must gather honey and store it for winter, just like the squirrel gathers and stores nuts.

When it gets cold, there are no flowers. The bees can not find nectar or pollen. Besides, their bodies become stiff and they can't fly. Bees that do not have enough honey in their hive to last until spring will not survive. They will die.

Bees have enemies. Certain kinds of ants like honey, and will destroy a weak hive in order to get it. Bears like honey, too. Sometimes they rob a hive in the fall, causing the bees to starve during the winter.

But ants and bears are not the bees' biggest enemy. It is man. Why would man want to harm these little insects that do so much good? Often he does not mean to harm them. He just does not stop to think what he is doing.

He sprays his fields to kill harmful insects, and he kills the bees, too. He
sprays poison on his fields to kill the
weeds. The poison gets on the flowers
and the bees get some of it when they
gather nectar. They get sick and die.
In some parts of the world, bees have
been driven away by insect and weed
sprays.

Many people have learned that these
poisons are harmful to the bees. They are
more careful in using them. They know
what helpful insects bees are, and they
do what they can to help them survive.

IF YOU WERE BUSY

If you were busy being kind,
Before you knew it, you would find
You'd soon forget to think it's true
That someone was unkind to you.

If you were busy being glad,
And cheering people who are sad,
Although your heart would ache a bit,
You'd soon forget to notice it.

If you were busy doing good,
And doing just the best you could,
You'd not have time to blame some man,
Who's also doing the best he can.

If you were busy doing right,
You'd find yourself too busy quite,
To criticize some neighbor long,
Because he's busy doing wrong.

Unit Four:

Climbing Higher

The Boy Who Was Afraid

Part 1: Big or Little?

Danny was a big boy for his age. At least, he was big in some ways. He was seven years old. He could milk a cow. He could carry feed for the chickens. He could fill the woodbox. He was even taller than most of the boys in the second grade at school.

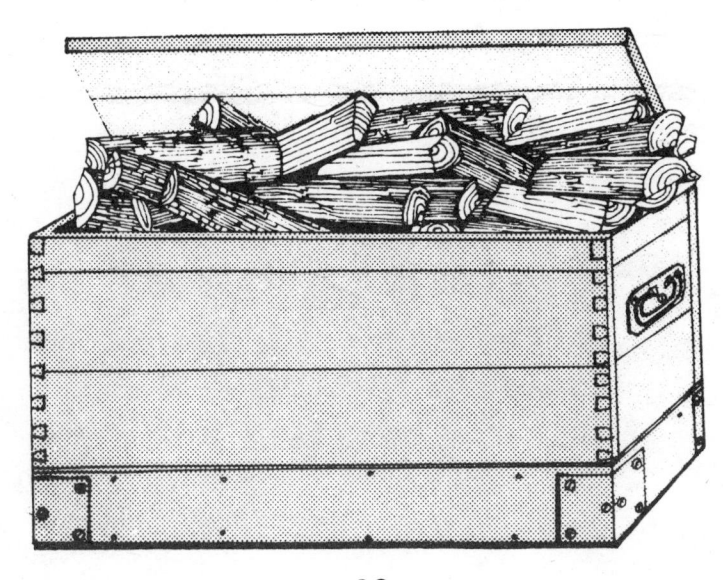

But in one way Danny was not big. He was afraid. Sometimes it seemed he was afraid of everything.

Danny was especially afraid after dark. But even in the daytime he was afraid to walk to the barn when all the rest of the family was in the house. He was also afraid to stay in the house if the others were outside.

Danny was afraid of shadows. He was afraid the wolves would come and get him. He was afraid a drunk man would come and take him away. He was even afraid the house would burn down.

Mother was patient. She often took time to explain to Danny that he should not be afraid. God was up in heaven and He could see everything on the earth. He took care of little boys, and did not let anything happen that was not good for them in one way or another. She said there were angels who watched over children and kept them from harm.

But Danny was still afraid.

Daddy tried to be patient, too. He explained to Danny that his fears did not make sense. He would take him on his knee and talk to him for a long while. He would tell Danny that the wolves were all far away. Besides, wolves were afraid of people. They ran away from them if they could. Daddy had never heard of a wolf killing a boy, or even biting him.

"Why are you afraid a drunk will come?" Daddy asked. "Have you ever seen one drive in the lane? And if one did come, why do you think he would want to hurt you?"

Danny could not answer these questions. All he knew was that he was afraid. He was so afraid that if he was alone in the house, he turned pale at any

little noise. He would begin to shake all over. His heart would beat very fast, and his throat would go dry.

Daddy and Mother loved Danny, but it was very unhandy to have a boy in the family who was so afraid. They could not leave him in the house with the younger children. They could not send him anywhere to get something.

"Worst of all," Mother said one day, "he is making the other children afraid, too. A year ago William wasn't afraid of anything, but now he is. I can't send him anywhere alone."

"I know," Daddy said sadly. "Danny needs help in getting over his fears. But how can we help him? We have tried and tried to tell him that the things he is afraid of are all imaginary."

"What else is there to do?" Mother asked.

"I don't know," Daddy said. "But I think we will soon have to try something else. I am about ready to give him a spanking for being so afraid. Maybe that would help."

"I don't know, but I do not think that will help," Mother said. "If Danny is mean, then a spanking will help. If he does not obey, or if he tells a lie, then we should spank, and spank hard. But for being afraid? I am afraid a spanking will only make it worse."

"Then we will have to be patient a while longer," Daddy said. "But I do not like it that he is making the other children afraid, too. One boy like that is enough."

Mother agreed. "Yes, one boy who is afraid is enough."

So Daddy and Mother talked some more to Danny. They explained again that his fears did not make sense. If he heard a noise that frightened him, Daddy took him by the hand and they went to see what it was.

One night Daddy took Danny out to the barnyard and showed him that the noise he heard was just the gate creaking on the hinges. Another time they went upstairs into a dark room and found out that the noise they had heard was just the window rattling in the wind.

A gate creaking on its hinges. A window rattling in the wind. Surely Danny could see that such things could not harm anyone, no matter how spooky they sounded.

But Danny was still afraid.

Part 2: One Dark Night

Then one day something happened which brought a change. It was not a big change, but at least it was a start.

It was on a Wednesday evening after school. Danny had made up his mind to be brave. Grandmother had come to visit. She lived a mile down the road. She asked Danny to go home with her. Grandfather would not be home when she got there, and she needed someone to help her with the horse. She was no longer young and spry, and the horse often did not stand still. She did not want to fall and hurt herself.

Danny wanted to go with Grandmother. He knew she needed his help. But he would have to walk home by himself. He was afraid. He looked at Mother, hoping she would explain why he could not go.

Mother did not say a word. She decided to let Danny do his own explaining. To her surprise, he said, "Yes, Grandmother, I will go with you. I will hold the horse for you."

So Danny went with Grandmother. He
surprised Mother. He surprised Daddy.
He even surprised himself! But it made
him feel good. He would get home somehow, even if he was afraid. Maybe he
could show the others that he wasn't a
baby after all.

Danny jumped off the buggy and held
the horse while Grandmother got off.
Then they tied the horse to the post.
Grandmother was very glad for Danny's
help. She told him to come into the

house. She wanted to give him a cookie. When they got there, she decided the cookie would taste better if he had chocolate milk to drink with it. And then she decided the milk would taste even better if it was hot.

It took a while to heat the milk. At last it was ready. How good it tasted to Danny. He did not hurry, because the milk was too hot to drink fast. Besides, he enjoyed sitting there, visiting with Grandmother.

Finally Danny was ready to start home. The minute he got outside, he wished he had not come. The sun had set and it had started to get dark. He was afraid. He was terribly afraid.

It was hard for Danny to keep from crying. But there was nothing else to do. He had to go home. Grandmother could not go with him. The longer he waited, the darker it would get.

Danny tried hard not to think about drunks and wolves as he ran down the road. He tried to think of God and the angels that were watching over him. He tried very, very hard to be brave.

Danny ran until he was out of breath. Then he walked fast. Everything was going fine. He didn't feel quite so afraid now. It was almost dark, but he was just about at home.

And then he heard it — the noise! It was loud and shrill. "Eeeeeeee-eeeeee-ooooooooo-eeeekkkkkkkk!"

Danny stopped in his tracks. He listened. He held perfectly still. He was afraid to move. In fact, he was almost too afraid to breathe. When the noise came the second time, it was so loud and shrill and seemed so close that Danny jumped right off the ground.

"Eeeeeeee-eeeeeee-oooooo-eeeekkkkkkkkk!"

Danny turned white. He shivered. His heart thumped and hammered inside his chest. He shook all over. He had never been so frightened in all his life. This time it was real. He wasn't just imagining it. The wolves were going to get him.

Once more the sound came, even closer this time. Danny was afraid to look around. He was sure that he would see the forms of the hungry beasts in the shadows of darkness. He wanted to run as he had never run before. But he didn't. He made himself think.

"No matter how fast I run, the wolves can run even faster," he thought. He reached down and picked up a handful of stones. Maybe if he threw stones at the wolves and yelled at them in a deep, gruff voice, they would think he was a big, strong man. Maybe they would be afraid of him. And maybe, just maybe, the angels would hold the wolves' mouths shut until he got home.

Danny forced himself to take a step, and then another one. Oh, how he wanted to run, but he didn't. He knew that would tell the wolves how afraid he was. Then they would jump on his back and get him for sure.

Danny reached the lane. The stones were still in his hand. He crossed the lawn, and got to the corner of the house. A few more steps and he would be safely inside the house. But then he decided to go to the barn. No one was in the house, and he didn't want to be there alone.

And then he heard it again. It was closer and more shrill than it had ever been before. In fact, this time it was close enough that he knew what it was — the windmill. He looked up at the wheel as it turned slowly in the wind. Now and then it gave out a shrill squeak.

Danny felt weak with relief and very,
very silly. He had been afraid of the
windmill! He even had to laugh a little.
He waited until he had gotten his breath,
then he went to the barn.

Daddy was milking the first cow. "Hi, Danny," he said. "I see you made it home all right."

William was sitting on the milk stool, holding a cat. "Weren't you afraid, walking home by yourself in the dark?" he asked.

Danny started to say, "No," but then he stopped. He knew that would be a big lie. "Yes-s, I — I was afraid," he said. "But I told myself to be brave, because there wasn't really anything to be afraid of."

Daddy had a pleased smile on his face. He winked at Mother, who was smiling, too. It almost seemed if they had planned that Grandmother would keep him there until it was almost dark. Danny never was quite sure about that, but it didn't matter. Never again was he so afraid in the dark, and he never again imagined a pack of wolves was after him.

The Missing Cupcakes

Part 1: A Treat for Everyone

It was Saturday afternoon. Rachel and Anna, the big girls in the family, were almost finished with their work. They weren't really big, because they were only seven and eight years old. But they were always called the big girls, because they were bigger than their twin sisters, Susan and Sara. The twins were four years old.

Susan and Sara had finished their work, and Mother had told them they could go play. She had said Rachel and Anna could play, too, as soon as they had their work done. They were still dusting the furniture in the living room.

"Mother, we're finished," Rachel said, putting the dusting cloth into the closet where it belonged.

"Good!" Mother exclaimed. She was mixing something in a bowl. "How would you like a special treat? You were good helpers today."

"Oh, goody! Cupcakes!" the girls exclaimed. They came over to where Mother was working.

"One, two, three, four," Mother counted, putting the cupcakes on the table. "One for each of you, and one for each of the twins."

"Thank you!" the girls said. They snatched up the cupcakes and ran out to find their sisters.

The twins were just as pleased as their sisters had been. Susan started licking the frosting. Sara peeled down the paper and took a bite.

"I'm not going to eat mine right away," Anna said. "I'm going to save it until later."

Susan nibbled on her cupcake. "Hmmm, this is good," she said.

"Let's go to the playhouse," Rachel suggested. Then after thinking a little, she added, "Anna and I will go first. Then Susan and Sara will come and be our guests. Knock on the door when you come, like Mrs. West does when she comes to buy eggs."

"All right," the twins agreed. They were used to having the older girls telling them what to do. They stood under the tree, nibbling and licking at their cupcakes. After a while they heard Anna call. "All right, girls, we are ready for you."

The twins went to the playhouse. They took what was left of the cupcakes with them. There were only a few small bites left over when they got there.

"You weren't supposed to eat your cupcakes," Rachel scolded when she came to
answer their knock. We wanted to sit
down and eat them together when you
come to visit."

Sara giggled. "We're guests, but we
were supposed to bring our own cupcakes," she said.

"Well, you're not going to get any of
ours," Rachel said. "You've eaten yours,
so you will just have to pretend you are
eating when we sit at the table."

That's as far as the girls got in their
game. The twins decided they didn't
want to play after all. It didn't sound
like fun, sitting there and watching the
older girls eat their cupcakes. They decided to go back to the sandbox.

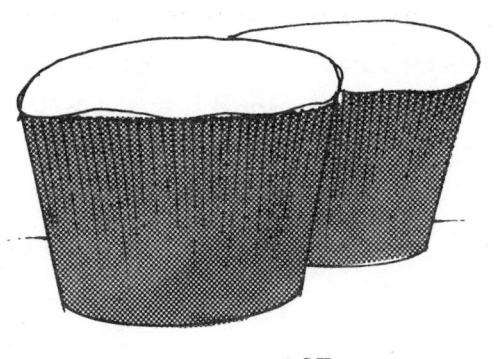

After the twins had left, Rachel and
Anna looked at each other. Rachel, who
was good at using her imagination, said,
"Let's play church. After church you
will come to my house, and we'll have
our cupcakes for a snack."

"Yes, let's," Anna said. They put the
cupcakes on the window sill. Then they
picked up their dolls and walked to the
shade tree in the yard. This is where
they always went to play church. There
was a little bench there, and it was just
the right place to play.

Meanwhile, Susan and Sara came back
to the playhouse. They saw the cupcakes
on the window sill. "Hmmm, I wish those
were ours," Susan said.

"I wish so, too," Sara said. "But I'm
not going to take one. That would be
very naughty."

"Yes, I know," Susan said. But she
remembered how good her cupcake had
tasted. How she wished she had another
one. Then she had an idea. "Let's go in
and ask Mom if we may have some more
cupcakes."

The girls ran toward the house as fast as they could go. Rachel and Anna saw them, but they did not pay any attention to them. They went right on playing church under the shade tree.

Mother did not give the twins another cupcake. "It will soon be supper time," she said.

"But we want to be Rachel and Anna's guests," Susan said. "We need something to eat while they eat their cupcakes."

Mother just smiled and said, "You have eaten yours, so you can't have more until it is supper time."

Sara and Susan were disappointed, but they knew Mother was right. They had eaten their cupcakes, so they did not have them anymore. They went back to the sandbox.

Part 2: The Mystery

After a while Rachel and Anna were
done playing church. They walked slowly back to the playhouse. They were
talking in make-believe voices, sounding
like grown-ups. Rachel asked Anna if
she had finished her spring house cleaning. Anna said she had wanted to finish
last week, but the children got sick and
she was busy taking care of them.

They both saw it at the same time. The cupcakes were gone! They stopped in their tracks, their eyes and their mouths open. "The twins took them," Anna said, sounding very upset.

"Of course they did," Rachel said. "Remember when we saw them running toward the house? They probably hid somewhere to eat them."

"I'm going to tell Mom," Anna said, putting the dolls in the playhouse and marching in through the yard. Rachel followed her. When they came around the corner of the house, they stopped in surprise. There were the twins in the sandbox, acting as if they had not done anything naughty.

"We're going to tell Mom what you did," Rachel said, sounding cross. "You're going to get a spanking."

"What did we do?" Sara asked. She looked surprised and hurt.

"You know what you did," Anna said. "We saw you running from the play-house."

"We just —" Sara began.

"Don't lie about it. We know you took the cupcakes." Rachel's voice was sharp.

"We did not!" both girls said together. Then Sara added, "We just looked at them. We didn't even touch them."

"Of course you touched them. You ate them," Anna said. "And you'd better not lie about it. You'll get a hard spanking if you do."

Susan began to cry.

"See, you're guilty, or you wouldn't cry," Rachel said. She went into the house to tell Mother what the twins had done.

By the time Mother and the big girls came out of the house, the twins were both crying. "We —we didn't do it," Susan sobbed.

Mother dried the twins' tears and told them to stop crying so they could talk about it. Sara and Susan told how they had looked at the cupcakes. Then they had gone to the house to ask Mother for some more cupcakes. When Mother had refused to give them some, they had gone back to the sandbox to play. That was where Rachel and Anna had found them.

Then the big girls told their story.
They had put the cupcakes on the window
sill and gone to play church. They had
seen the twins go to the playhouse. A
little later they had seen them run away
to hide the cupcakes.

"W-we d-didn't have the cupcakes
when we r-ran to the house," Sara said.
She started to cry again.

"Shhh!" Mother said. "Let's go out to
the playhouse. Maybe the cupcakes just
fell off the window sill. Did you look on
the ground outside the playhouse?"

Rachel and Anna followed Mother and
the twins to the playhouse. They had
been so sure the twins had taken the cupcakes. But now they started to wonder.
What if they had just fallen off the window sill? What if the twins were telling
the truth after all?

They had not even reached the playhouse when Anna saw something blowing
in the breeze. "See, here is the wrapper," she said, running over to pick it
up. It was badly torn, but anyone could
see that it was a cupcake wrapper.

Mother looked carefully at the piece of torn paper. Then she reached down and picked up some more bits of the same paper. A look of understanding crossed her face. "Your cupcakes are gone, all right," she said. "But you are not blaming the right thief. It was our naughty puppy who ate them. The twins would not have chewed up the wrapper like this.

The twins smiled with relief. Their faces shone. "See, we were not lying after all," Susan said.

Rachel and Anna looked at each other. Anna said, "If the dog ate our cupcakes,

may we each have another one? We
didn't even get one little taste of them."

"No, you may not," Mother said.
"Doing without cupcakes is part of your
punishment for blaming the twins when
they weren't guilty."

"But we didn't know it wasn't them,"
Rachel said.

"Nor did you know that it was," Mother
said. "We must always be very sure before we blame anyone for something. You
made the twins feel very badly, when
they hadn't done anything naughty at
all."

Anna and Rachel looked at the ground.
They did not say anything.

"Tell the twins you are sorry," Mother
said. "Then you had better come to the
house with me the rest of the afternoon.
Maybe that will help you remember not to
blame anyone until you are sure they are
guilty."

The big girls told the twins they were
sorry. Then they followed Mother into
the house. Their playing time was over
for that afternoon.

Joseph Tattles on Himself

Joseph sat down at the breakfast table. He still looked sleepy, because he had just gotten out of bed. He was eight, but he did not always have to get up to help chore in the morning. David and Robert, who were older, always had to get up to help.

"I'm going to a sale today," Dad said, looking at Mother. "Do you have any work for the boys?"

"I could use some help in the potato patch," Mother said. "But that won't take all day."

"All right. The boys can clean the potato patch this forenoon," Dad said. "When they are done they may go fishing for the rest of the day. That is, if they still want to go fishing."

"Oh, yes, yes," David and Robert said. They had been begging to go fishing for weeks.

"May I go along, too?" Joseph asked. "Please, Dad, I want to."

"Well," Dad said, looking at Mother.

"He will fall into the water and drown," David said.

"No, I won't," Joseph said. "Please, Dad. I want to go along."

"All right, you may," Dad said. "But you will have to help hoe the potato patch. And be sure you stay out of the water. The pond is deep at places and it isn't safe for you to go in."

"I won't," Joseph said. He was very excited.

The potatoes had never been hoed so fast as they were that forenoon. When the boys came in at half past ten and said they were finished, Mother could not believe it. They took her by the hand and almost dragged her to the potato patch. She was surprised and pleased. "You are finished, and you have done a very good job," she said.

"Joseph pulled the weeds and we did the hoeing," David said. "You should have seen him work!"

Mother smiled. "What are you going to do now until dinner time?" she asked.

"Go fishing," Robert said. "Couldn't we pack our lunches and go now? We'll come home earlier if we may."

"All right," Mother agreed. "I was just going to make sandwiches and a few things like that. You might as well take your lunches along and eat at the pond."

Now Joseph was even more excited. He helped Mother make sandwiches and chocolate milk. By the time they were

finished, the older boys had dug worms.
Soon they were on their way.

Joseph felt very important as he walked
between his older brothers. They went
down the road, then cut across a field.
Next they climbed a hill and went
through the woods. Then they went down
the hill through another field. At last
they were at the pond.

David and Robert put worms on their
hooks and started to fish. David offered
to help Joseph, but he was sure he didn't
need any help. He was old enough to do
it by himself. However, after trying a
long time, he gave up. "David, help me
with this slippery worm," he said. "If it
would hold still, I could do it. But it
keeps wiggling."

David put a worm on Joseph's hook.
Joseph threw the hook into the water and
watched the bobber sharply. He expected
a fish to come along right away. He
waited. He pulled the hook out of the
water to see if he had a fish. He didn't,
so he threw the hook back in. In a minute he pulled it out again.

"Hold your line still," Robert said. "You'll never catch a fish that way."

Joseph didn't think it was fun, standing there on the bank of the pond, doing nothing. The sun was very warm as it shone from a cloudless sky. Soon the boys were hungry and thirsty. They decided to eat their lunch.

"The fish don't seem to be biting today," David said. "I'm going over to the other side of the pond."

220

"I'm going over there, too," Joseph said, eager to do something. But the fish didn't bite on the other side either.

"What are we going to do?" Joseph asked, sounding impatient. "Sit here and do nothing all afternoon?"

"No, we'll sit here and fish," David said, grinning at his brother.

"But what if they don't bite?" Joseph asked.

"We'll keep on trying." David put a fresh worm on his hook and tossed it into the water again. "One time we came here and fished for three hours before we had a nibble. But when they started, they kept right on biting. We took seven nice fish home that evening."

Joseph decided to wait until they started biting. He pulled in his line and wound it on the pole. Then he rolled up his pant legs and waded into the water.

"Joseph, you'd better be careful," Robert said. "Didn't Dad tell you to stay out of the water?"

"He meant the deep water," Joseph said. "It's not deep here. I can see the bottom." He waded around a little more. Then he asked, "Are you going to tattle on me?"

"We might, if you don't get out of the water," David said. "You'll scare the fish away."

"I'll go up the bank a little ways," Joseph said. He ran a short distance away, then he waded into the water again. He was careful that his pant legs didn't get wet. If that happened, Dad and Mother would find out that he had been in the water. He didn't want that to happen.

Joseph waded in a little deeper. He forced his pant legs up a little further and took a few more steps. Then suddenly and without warning, the ground seemed to slip from under Joseph's feet. He was falling into the water — deeper, deeper, deeper. He could not even reach the bottom with his feet.

"HELP!" shouted Joseph. And then even his head and face were under the water. He thrashed around. Where was he, and what was happening? He wanted to breathe, but he couldn't.

Then something big grabbed Joseph by the shirt. Was it a big fish, trying to drag him deeper into the water? He struggled and twisted, trying to get free.

Suddenly he was out of the water. He could breathe again. He opened his eyes and looked up. There was David, standing beside him on the bank. David was dripping wet, too.

"W-what h-happened?" Joseph asked weakly.

"That's what I'd like to know," David said. His breath was coming in gasps. "I suppose you stepped into a hole and lost your balance. It's a good thing I happened to see you go, or I wouldn't have known where to look for you. It could easily have been too late by the time I found you."

Joseph shivered, both from being wet and from fright. David saw him shiver and said, "We'd better go home the fastest way possible. You're cold, and I'd like to get some dry clothes, too."

"No, let's stay here. Our clothes will dry," Joseph said. Going home was the last thing he wanted to do.

David, however, did not change his mind. He insisted on going home, and Robert agreed with him. "You were afraid we would tattle on you, Joseph," he said. "But now we don't have to. You'll tattle on yourself."

It did not take Mother long to guess what had happened. And of course, she wanted to know if Joseph had fallen in by accident, or how it had happened.

David made Joseph explain it by himself. Mother was even more frightened than the boys had been. "Just think. You could have drowned," she said soberly. "You disobeyed Dad, so you'll just have to wait until he comes home for your punishment."

The afternoon was a long one. It was so different from what Joseph had expected it to be. Instead of sitting by the pond, pulling one fish after the other from the water, he sat on the porch steps, waiting for Dad to come home and punish him. Mother explained that since he had disobeyed, he had spoiled the fun for himself and for the other boys, too.

As it turned out, Joseph hadn't spoiled the fun for only one day. For his punishment Dad said he had to wait a whole year before he went fishing with the older boys again. "You will have to wait until you are old enough to be trusted," Dad said. "It will be at least a year. Maybe longer."

About a week later David and Robert were allowed to go fishing again. This was to make up for the time they had to come home with Joseph. And of course, they went without Joseph this time.

Joseph watched his brothers leave. It was hard for him to keep from crying. He was even more sad when they came home with ten nice, big fish. But he knew it was his own fault. He decided it was better to obey after that.

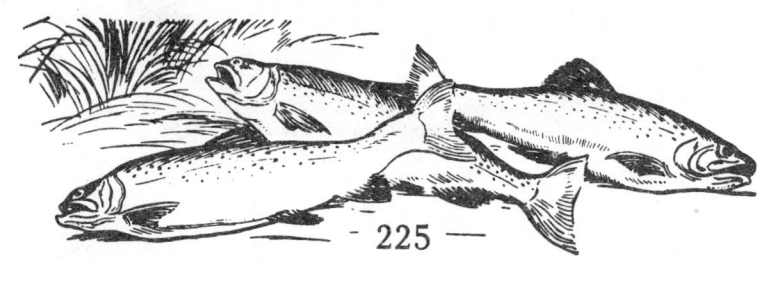

Melinda Learns to Be Thankful

"Melinda, Melinda! Where are you?" called Mother. She was in the garden, getting ready to plant seeds.

"Yes, I'm coming," answered a sleepy ten-year-old from the living room, where she had been reading a book.

"Please come and help me plant these peas," Mother said.

Melinda groaned. Why did she always have to be working? Ever since school was out Mother kept her busy from morning until night. Well, almost. They had time to read and play and do whatever they wanted to now and then. But they had to help Mother much of the time.

The early May sun felt good on Melinda's back as she worked, but she couldn't keep from grumbling. "Why are we planting so many peas?" she asked. "Just think of all the hoeing we will have to do. Then we will have to break our backs picking the peas. And I can already feel how my thumb is going to hurt from shelling them. Last year it got sore and red when we had two bushels to shell in one day."

"Melinda," Mom said, her voice sounding firm and a little sad. She had tried many times to break Melinda's habit of grumbling. "Let's be thankful that we can raise food to eat. Instead of thinking about all the work that goes with gardening, I like to think of what we will get from it."

Melinda had to agree; fresh vegetables from the garden were a treat. But she could not enjoy the long hours of hard work that came before they could have those vegetables.

The days passed. Melinda forgot about the backache of planting peas. She was excited when she saw the first green plants peeping up through the ground after a refreshing shower. Each day they grew a little, and then the rows could easily be seen.

The day came when the peas had to be hoed for the first time. Melinda helped, and she did not grumble. However, by the time the garden had been hoed the second and third times, she grumbled a lot. Each day seemed to be warmer than the day before. Melinda could not forget how nice it would be to curl up under the shade tree with a book, or go for a walk with the younger children.

"Mother, the weeds are growing faster than any of the other things," Melinda grumbled again one forenoon while they were working in the garden. "I wish they would stop growing this very minute."

"If the weeds would stop growing, so would everything else in the garden," Mother said.

"I wouldn't care," Melinda muttered to herself. But she didn't say it out loud. She knew better than letting Mother hear her talk like that. But right then she was too warm and too tired and too upset to keep herself from thinking the things she was not allowed to say out loud.

That day as Melinda grumbled to herself, she had no idea that her wish would come true. The weeds didn't stop in one minute, but they did stop growing. For a whole week there was no rain. Dad and the boys made hay fast, talking about the perfect haying weather. But long after

the hay was all in the barn, the good
haying weather continued. The sun shone
out of a cloudless sky and a warm wind
blew. Another week passed and then
another.

"If it does not rain soon, our corn will
suffer from the dry weather," Dad said,
looking at the sky for signs of rain. "The
leaves are curling up already."

"It has been dry at this time of the year before, but the rain came soon enough to save at least part of the crop," Mother said hopefully. "The garden is drying up. I would water it, but where would I start in such a big garden? Besides, if it stays dry all summer, we'll have to save our water or the well will go dry."

One day Melinda remembered that they had not hoed the garden for a long time. She decided to go see if there were any weeds. She could not believe what she saw. The cabbage plants that had looked so promising lay flat on the ground. The peas were turning yellow at the stems. The potato and tomato plants were drooping. The ground was dry and dusty, just like the road. A feeling of sadness and dread filled her heart.

"Mother, did you see how the garden looks?" Melinda asked, going into the house. "The peas and tomatoes and everything look sick."

"They are suffering from the dry weather," Mother answered. "It hasn't been this dry for years."

Another week passed without rain, and then another. If Melinda had thought the garden looked poor, it was to look much poorer. The lawn turned brown, and here and there the earth had big cracks.

Then it was time to harvest the peas, but there were none to harvest. The lettuce that was there tasted bitter, and no one liked it. Mother started to make potato soup instead of mashed or fried potatoes, because she said the old potatoes were nearly all and the new ones were a very small crop. By making soup, she could stretch the potatoes a little further.

Whenever Melinda talked of opening a jar of corn or peas from the basement, Mother shook her head. "We have to save them as much as we can. We may not get any vegetables to can this year."

Dad, too, was concerned about the dry weather. Since the grass in the pastures did not grow anymore, he had to feed the hay he had put away for the winter. By now it was plain that there would not be much of a corn crop, which meant they would have to buy feed for the livestock.

232

With no yard to mow, no garden to hoe, and no vegetables to can, Melinda had plenty of free time. But she did not enjoy it. It was too warm to play or to go on walks. She did not feel like reading.

Even though her parents did not complain about the weather, or even talk much about it, Melinda sensed that they were concerned. How were they going to make ends meet if they had to buy so much food for themselves and the livestock? She had heard Dad say that hay and straw and grain were all going to be expensive.

Then one evening, after an extra warm day, thunder clouds stood in the west. Melinda watched them from her window before she went to bed. She got an uneasy feeling. Would they have a storm? Would it really rain, or would the clouds blow away, like they had so many times before?

Sometime during the night Melinda awoke and heard it rain. The drops were beating down on the roof. The lightning

flashed and the thunder cracked. Melinda was filled with gladness. It was raining at last!

The next morning when the Millers got up, it was still raining. It came down more gently now, and the grass in the yard was a little green already. When Dad came in for breakfast, he announced that it had rained two inches already. "We're getting a real soaker, and it's not over yet," he said. "It might rain all day."

It did. All that week showers came up at any time of the day or night. The sun shone brightly between the showers, bringing about a miracle Melinda could hardly believe.

Some of the plants that had looked brown and dead, turned green and started to grow. Others did not. As soon as the ground dried off, the Millers went into the garden. They pulled out the dead plants and put in new seeds. "If we have enough rain and a late frost, we'll still get some vegetables," Mother said.

Melinda worked with Mother. She planted seeds and covered them with the moist soil. She pulled and hoed weeds. When the grass in the yard needed to be mowed, she did her share. She did all this, and she did not complain once.

The dry summer had cured Melinda of the habit of grumbling. She had learned that when there was no work on the farm or in the garden, there was no harvest. And when there was no harvest, there was nothing to eat. She understood now what Mom meant when she told her to be thankful that they had work to do.

235

Cows Are Cows

Part 1: Greedy Animals

Even though it was cold and windy out-
doors, Marvin worked in his shirt sleeves.
The cows and the horses in the barn made
the place feel warm. Besides, Marvin was
working hard. He had thrown down hay
and straw. Now he was filling the metal
bushel basket with silage and dragging it
down the feed aisle to each cow. He had
to drag it, because it was much too heavy
for him to carry.

"Marvin, would you please come and
give this milk to the calves?" his sister
Ella called. "I need the bucket to milk
Rose."

"Sure," Marvin said. He went over
and got the milk. He poured it into two
buckets and walked over to the calf pens.
The four calves all came eagerly. The
biggest one bossed the others away. Then
she stretched her neck over the side of
the pen toward the buckets.

"Oh, no, you don't," Marvin said, giving her a kick. "You should know by this time that you have to wait until last. If you'd learn to use better manners, I'd feed you first." He picked up the strap he had there and made the greedy calf go back. Then he fed two of the smaller ones. The biggest calf tried to get her nose into the pail, too, but Marvin hit her with the strap to make her go away.

Dad came into the barn and saw what a hard time Marvin was having. He came to help. "Has this one had her milk?" he asked, pushing her back with his hand. He was more gentle about it than Marvin had been.

"No, these are the first two," Marvin answered.

"I think you'd find it easier to feed the biggest ones first," Dad advised. "Then they'd no longer be so hungry when you feed the last two."

Marvin didn't answer. He didn't tell Dad that he was trying to teach the big calf better manners. A little later he came back with milk for the other calves. The bossy one stuck her head into the pail and drank greedily. When she was about half finished, she gave the pail a bump with her head. She splashed milk on herself and on Marvin.

"All right. That's all you get," Marvin said, making her quit drinking. He let one of the other calves have the rest of the milk.

The bossy calf had the habit of spilling some of her milk, and Marvin was trying to break her of it by not letting her have the rest of the milk. But somehow, so far it hadn't done much good. If anything, the calf was more greedy than ever.

Marvin set the empty pails aside and went back to feeding the cows. He worked fast, like he always did. He enjoyed doing his chores, and he always liked to see how soon he could have them done. He enjoyed working with animals, except when they didn't act right. One of the animals he didn't like was the bossy calf. And there was a cow that was almost as bad. Or maybe she was a little worse. Marvin couldn't decide.

It was Horny, who stood right in the middle of the long row of cows. Marvin always started feeding the cows at the far end. Every time he dragged a basket full of silage down the aisle, Horny reached out and tried to grab a bite.

Tonight Horny was as bad as ever. She kept straining on her chain, wagging her head from one side to the other. She showed in every way she could that she was very hungry. When Marvin fed Rose, who stood next to Horny, she dropped down on her knees and tried to get some of the silage. Marvin knew she would, and put the feed far enough away that she couldn't reach it.

The next basket full should have been Horny's, but just before Marvin dumped it in front of her, he changed his mind. "You're going to wait until last," he said through his teeth. "That will teach you not to be so impatient." He skipped Horny and gave the silage to the next cow. He was careful to put it far enough away so that Horny couldn't reach it.

Marvin stood and watched the cow, chuckling to himself. She stretched first one way and then the other, trying to get some feed. Even though she stretched her tongue until it seemed to be a foot long, she couldn't reach a single mouth full.

"Keep trying," Marvin said, going on
with his work. He wasn't quite finished
feeding the cows when someone called
his name. Grabbing his coat, he hurried
outside to see what was going on.

Part 2: Not Like People

It didn't take him long to see what the
trouble was. Half a dozen pigs were running around outside their pen. Jerry,
who was a few years older than Marvin,
was standing by the door of the hog house,

trying to keep the others from coming out, too.

"Stupid pigs!" Marvin muttered, grabbing a stick to use as a club. "That's what I don't like about hogs. They want to be everywhere except in their pens where they are supposed to be."

Marvin took off after the first pig on the run. It wasn't hard to circle her and start her back. He whacked her with his club. She ran toward the hog house without any trouble, but she ran right on past. She didn't even slow down. Jerry tried to stop her by waving his hands and shouting, but she didn't seem to see him.

"Why didn't you stop her?" Marvin asked, sounding cross.

"I couldn't. You chased her too fast," Jerry answered. "You'll never get them in that way. Dad always says you can't hurry a pig."

Marvin ran after the pig the second time, calling Sport to help him. It didn't take the dog long to circle the pig and head her back, but it did no good. She ran right on past again.

By this time Dad and the girls had come
to help. The first thing Dad did was call
Sport back. "We don't need your help,"
he said. "Stay back."

Dad, Marvin, and the girls made a big
circle around the pigs. "Steady now,"
Dad said. "Don't hurry them. They need
time to make up their minds. Before they
decide to go in, we can chase them all
over the place. Let's try to keep them in
our circle."

Soon the pigs were at the doorway.
Jerry stood back and joined the circle,
which was getting smaller and smaller.
The hogs woof, woofed and sniffed the

ground. Marvin longed to give them a whack over the head with his club so they would hurry. Standing there and waiting on them to make up their minds did not agree with him. But Dad didn't let him. "Give them time," he said in a low, steady voice. "They will go in if we don't rush them. You can't hurry a pig."

The pigs finally went in, but Marvin was feeling pretty disgusted by that time. "They ought to go without feed for a week," he said. "That would teach them not to break out."

Dad heard what Marvin had said. "They'd break out for sure then," he said. "I'm afraid punishing animals doesn't work the way we want it to. Hogs are hogs, and you can't train them to be anything else."

"At least they could be well-mannered hogs," Marvin said.

Dad chuckled. "I'm afraid well-mannered hogs are pretty hard to find," he said. "You see, there is a difference between human nature and animal nature. Humans can think. They can figure things out. But animals can't do that. They are — well, I guess they are just animals."

"They are smart enough to find a hole in the fence if there is one, or to make one if they possibly can," Marvin thought, going back to the barn. He tried to re-member what he had been doing when Jerry called him. Then he knew. He had been feeding the cows.

Marvin had forgotten all about Horny. He ran to the barn, wondering if she was still twisting and turning her head, trying to get feed from the cows beside her.

She wasn't. She was standing at the feed box, helping herself to all she wanted. "Look. Horny's loose!" Marvin called. "How did she do that?"

Marvin ran to her stall to see what was wrong. She had broken her chain. He felt a little guilty, because he knew it was partly his fault. If he had fed her, it wouldn't have happened.

Dad came into the barn and helped Marvin put Horny back into her stall. Then he asked the question Marvin was afraid he would ask. "Did you forget to give her feed? Surely she hasn't cleaned it all up yet."

Marvin was tempted to say he had forgotten, but his conscience didn't let him do that. He knew that wasn't the truth. He said, "I — I made her wait until last. She is always so greedy and I'm trying to break her of it."

Dad smiled a little. "That won't help. Feed her first, then she will be satisfied and won't give you any trouble. Then you can feed the rest of the cows in peace."

"But why does she have to be so greedy?" Marvin asked. "The rest of the cows aren't."

"Cows are like people — not all alike," Dad answered. "I know animals can be trained to do certain things, but you can't make them act like people. You may think you are punishing Horny and the bossy calf by making them wait until last, but you aren't. You are only trying to get even with them. It is not changing them a bit, and it only makes your chores harder for you."

Marvin watched while Dad took a piece of wire and fixed Horny's chain.

"As I said a while ago, human nature can be changed," Dad went on. "With God's help, we can become better people. But with animals, it doesn't work that way. The thing to do is change our way of acting and get along with our animals the best we can. As long as we try to make them behave like people, we will not get along with them."

Marvin finished his chores. He was thinking about what Dad had said. It made sense. The last while he hadn't allowed the bossy calf to finish her milk. That only made her more hungry and greedy than ever.

It was the same way with Horny. He had put feed where she could see it, but she could not reach it. Maybe it was no wonder she had broken her chain. She was just acting like a cow, and a hungry one at that.